When Being a Nurse Was Fun

Tales From My Life as a Nurse

Ann Watt

To Sherie
Enjoy the book and
have fun at The Big E!
Ann Watt
Sept 15, 2023

Visit our website at
www.StillwaterPress.com
for more information.

First Stillwater River Publications Edition

ISBN: 978-1-960505-18-7

Library of Congress Control Number: 2023907608

Names: Watt, Ann, 1967- author.
Title: When being a nurse was fun : tales from my life as a nurse /
    Ann Watt.
Description: First Stillwater River Publications edition. |
    Pawtucket, RI, USA : Stillwater River Publications, [2023]
Identifiers: ISBN: 978-1-960505-18-7 | LCCN: 2023907608
Subjects: LCSH: Watt, Ann, 1967- | Women nurses--United
    States--Biography. | Nursing--United States--Anecdotes. |
    LCGFT: Autobiographies. | Anecdotes.
Classification: LCC: RT37.W378 A3 2023 | DDC: 610.73092-
    -dc23

1 2 3 4 5 6 7 8 9 10
Written by Ann Watt.
Cover and interior design by Elisha Gillette.
Published by Stillwater River Publications,
Pawtucket, RI, USA.

You have departed this life on Earth,
but you are not forgotten
Thank you for your contributions to healthcare:

Cathy Poirier, RN
Karla Carroll, RN, CRNA
Gail Mostertz, RN, CCRN
Carol Pierson-Riel RN, NP
Roberta Mayotte, RN
Maryse Confidant, RN
Lisa Cunningham, RN
Laurie Parillo, RN
Marjorie Hammond, RN
Nicole Thompson, RN, NP
Pauline Tanner
Chip Roberge
Gordon Wallace, PA-C
Dr. Leon Puppi
Dr. Jana Hudcova
Dr. Misbah Quadri
Dr. Marlene Cutitar

Table of Contents

Foreword

Over the years, I've often thought about writing a book about my experiences in the nursing profession. With each passing year, more tales were added to my memory bank, and it is finally time to share them with you. It is my sincerest hope that my audience enjoys the stories I have written, because it was my pleasure remembering them and putting them into print.

I admit that it was sometimes difficult choosing which events I wanted to describe, because I have enough stories to fill at least two lengthy books. I was a critical care nurse for thirty years, and there is no shortage of circumstances about which I could write. For the sake of privacy, I have not divulged specific details about individuals, although I've tried to keep my tales accurate. Any similarities to certain people may be merely coincidental. I honestly admit that I don't remember the true names of the patients who are mentioned in this book. Respectfully, I also acknowledge that they may no longer be living because a decade or more has passed since I cared for those patients.

The medical staff about whom I write may recognize themselves in my stories. Most of the names have been changed, and I have purposely not included any last names. I understand that my former colleagues may remember some of the occasions I have described, and that their perspective on what happened may be different than mine. We all remember things our own personal way. This book is about how I viewed various events, and highlights what was important to me.

My career as a nurse showed me the importance of being able to laugh at yourself and make the best of almost any situation. Staff nurses played jokes on each other and were amused by circumstances which might make other people angry or disgusted. Finding humor where there sometimes is none is a characteristic most nurses share. My former colleagues and I are proof that you can have fun and enjoy work while providing excellent care. The laughter we shared also brought us closer together.

This collection of stories, while mostly comical, also demonstrates the wide range of emotions a nurse may feel while at work or off duty. Nurses are humans with feelings. Occasionally, sorrow or frustration is unavoidable and a situation cannot be made comical.

I never regretted becoming a nurse, and I had a very fulfilling career. Any life path you choose will have its ups and downs. Pick a career which will bring you overall joy and challenge you to become a better person.

Thanks to all the current or retired nurses for your service. Best wishes to those of you who are pursuing a career as a nurse. Hopefully, some of my audience will be inspired to enter this worthwhile profession or specialize in critical care.

The Beginning

When I finally opened my eyes and looked around, it took me a few moments to become aware of where I was. I was lying on the floor of the angiography room, and there was a clamor of activity all around me. Looking up, I saw the elderly gentleman on the examination table peering down at me with concern on his face, asking, "Lady, you okay?"

Once they realized my eyes were open, a couple nurses assisted me onto a stretcher and promptly escorted me out of the room. They were taking me to the ER to be examined by an MD and get a CT scan of my head. I didn't really have to ask, "What happened to me?" because I already knew. I had passed out in the cardiac procedure room.

Oh boy. I'm in deep trouble now. That, and many other thoughts were swimming around in my head,

Ann and Karren in their dorm room

temporarily pushing out the pain I soon started feeling in my face. *This can't be happening to me. I worked so hard to get into college. Am I going to get kicked out of the nursing program? What am I going to do now? I don't want to move back home, I finally got away from there. I want to live my own life. I don't want to be stuck in some dead-end job. I don't have any money—is my health insurance going to cover the cost of this?*

Pain, somehow, also gets pushed aside in a young woman's brain when a handsome doctor with deep, sapphire blue eyes looks straight into her own. He was attempting to perform a neurologic exam and was checking my pupils, informing me that he needed to put some sutures in my chin, but that I'd receive some numbing medicine and it wasn't going to hurt.

I acknowledged his comments and questions, and

stated, "I feel okay, but the left side of my face really hurts."

He wasn't surprised and informed me that I had fractured my mandible and had many broken teeth, as well.

Under normal circumstances, if you broke your jaw, it would probably be wired shut for several weeks. You might also need to spend a day or two in the hospital. Still being a little dazed after passing out, I don't recall if I was given a choice whether I wanted my jaw wired or not. Someone probably made the decision for me. No wiring was initiated, and I was urged to keep my mouth mostly shut while the injury healed. It was also recommended that I stick to a liquid diet.

Many months would pass before my teeth were completely fixed. After seeing a dentist, I learned I would need root canals and caps on several of my broken teeth. For now, some temporary bonding was placed on the affected teeth, then I was discharged home from the ER.

"Home," at the present time, was my dorm room at Fitchburg State College (FSC), which is currently known as Fitchburg State University. My roommate, Karren, inquired what happened to me, and I retold the events of that embarrassing and traumatic morning. Since she was also a nursing student and knew what kind of existence we endured while earning our degree, I was gratefully spared a lecture.

No one at the hospital where the incident happened understood what I was going through at the time, and

I didn't exactly feel like explaining much to anyone except Dr. Blue-Eyes. A few staff members scolded me, telling me I should have consumed more food for breakfast, and that if I wasn't feeling well, I should have excused myself from the room before I passed out. They truly could not see things from my perspective.

Earlier that month—barely two weeks ago, as a matter of fact—my father finally died. His eleven-year battle with cancer of the larynx (along with cigarette smoking's detrimental effects on his health) were mercifully over.

It was April 1987, and I was a sophomore in college. I had needed to take a week off from school after my father's death in order to help my mother with funeral arrangements, sort through bills, and provide her with emotional support. There was no one else she could rely on to do the things that needed to be done. She had grown up in Poland and most of her relatives still lived there. The few family members we had in Massachusetts were not useful; they were either elderly themselves or didn't have the desire to assist her with funeral plans. She had a couple neighborhood friends and acquaintances from the local church community, but didn't want to bother them with any of her problems or questions. Therefore, the responsibility of helping my mother fell squarely on my shoulders.

If I could have passed those duties on to anyone else, I gladly would have done so at the time. I was only twenty years old and didn't know anything about the things with which she needed help. My father had always taken care of the household finances. Neither my mother nor I knew anything about his health insurance or medical claim forms. Questions regarding social security benefits cropped up. The decisions which needed to be made regarding the funeral itself were overwhelming. What kind of casket or flower arrangement did we want? Did he have a favorite hymn or Bible passage which should be read in church? How many calling hours did we want for the wake at the funeral home? Day to day, it was all a blur, and I bumbled my way through it with Mom the best I could.

Despite the circumstances, my mother enjoyed having me back at home for a week. I'm thankful she loved me as much as she did, and I cared about her in return. However, her love was suffocating me. I understood she was lonely, but she was clingy and desired to spend every moment of each day with me. She was acting as if I was home on vacation and wanted me to cook with her or sit and watch TV together. It was impossible telling her I needed some personal space and time to study without her interpreting it as rejection. She was heartbroken and psychologically needy after losing her husband. I was emotionally drained, and each long day that passed by felt like ten.

I felt bad when I left my mother and returned to school, although I was happy to be back at college. It was important for me to finish the spring semester, which would be over in mid-May. After that, I'd have the entire summer off and be free to spend time with her and help her resolve any remaining issues.

Mom had seen the pile of books I had brought home with me. I had anticipated that I would have some solitary time when I could concentrate on my schoolwork. I was progressing toward earning my Bachelor of Science degree in Nursing in order to become an RN, and the nursing program involved an immense amount of reading and preparation for classes. My freshman year was filled with a lot of basic elective courses, but the second year became much more demanding. Microbiology and Statistics were two of the required courses, and each was difficult for me. Passing grades were required in both of those classes in order to advance to my junior year of college, and I feared falling behind and failing.

As a sophomore, I was also finally taking "real" nursing courses and was participating in practical scenarios in actual hospitals. Mostly the hospital portion consisted of observation of procedures, and that's what I was doing in the angiography room when I fainted.

The day before my accident, I was rather excited to have the opportunity to watch the procedure, never having seen anything like that before. But I knew it was going to be a long day, even before the incident. My roommate Karren and I had slightly different schedules. We were generally taking the same classes, but while mine started late in the day, hers were much earlier. In this spring semester, it was my turn to have the early classes and practicums, and hers were later. Not wanting to disturb her, I crept around in mostly darkness as I prepared to get to Worcester. I had to wake up very early in order to get to the hospital on time, and nursing students didn't dare be late. My parents had always emphasized the importance of being prompt, and I also agreed with that notion. If you're on time, you're already late. You need to arrive early, and I dislike feeling rushed.

Having prepared most of the things I needed the night before, I grabbed a quick snack and headed directly to my car. Even though I pre-paid for the college's meal plan at the dining hall, the dining hall wouldn't open until about two hours after I left Fitchburg. It wasn't very user-friendly for nursing students, who had schedules which were different from most of the students who attended FSC. The best I could do was grab a few non-perishable items or perhaps a couple pieces of fruit from the cafeteria the previous day, which I could temporarily store in our small dorm room refrigerator. Stopping at a fast food restaurant for breakfast was not in my budget, and I doubt they were open at that early hour, either. Sure, I probably should have eaten more food that morning, but I didn't eat much, anyway. I was tall and rail thin, and I liked looking that way.

The problem I had with angiography was the room and atmosphere itself. Prior to entering that area, I was covered with a lead-weighted vest and skirt to protect me from any radiation exposure. Then I was told to stand quietly in a corner and "don't touch anything." I dutifully did as I was told, standing out of the way with my hands in the pockets of my nursing uniform. The patient, a kindly looking gentleman, was wheeled into the room and transferred to the procedure table. After what seemed like an eternity, a tall, authoritative figure—the medical cardiologist—made his grand entrance. I found him intimidating, and didn't need to be reminded to stay silent and pretend to be invisible.

The procedure, from my perspective, was not off to a smooth start. Despite what I imagine was a tremendous amount of skill, the doctor was unable to thread an access catheter. He seemed to get frustrated and was barking out orders to the staff. Perhaps the patient had some unusual anatomy or difficult blood vessels due to his advanced age. I didn't know enough about medicine at the time to understand the problem. All I knew was that I was feeling very hot, then cold, and then hot again. Was someone manipulating the thermostat? The room needed to be cool because of the equipment, and the protective gear was heavy and hot. But the patient was cold.

I was starting to think that I needed to leave the room because the procedure was taking too long, and I had been standing in the corner for quite a while. *How do I sneak out of the room without being noticed?* If I distracted the irritated doctor, I felt as though Hell's fury would be unleashed upon me. Not to mention my nursing instructor, who would probably give me demerits when she found out I didn't stay for the entire procedure. *What should I do?* I didn't have time to answer that question.

Without warning, I blacked out. I imagine I fell with a huge crash, like a redwood tree being cut in a forest. With my hands still in my pockets, I came lumbering to the ground, barely missing the corner of a metal table. I vaguely recall someone saying, "Who knew there would be that much blood from a cut on the chin?"

GREAT.

After eventually being notified that my jaw and many teeth were broken, I was fairly confident that my future nursing career was over before it started. Was the nursing class administrator going to kick me out of college? I was petrified of what was going to happen to me regarding school. Having recently spent a week at home helping out my mother after my father died, I knew I didn't want to return to Deerfield and permanently live there. I was moving on with life, I was enjoying college, and I was beginning to favor the fast-paced city of Worcester. The stress of a parent's death, and now the stress of this incident, were almost too much to bear.

Discussing my predicament with my advisor, I was notified that I could remain at FSC as long as I kept up with the required schoolwork for my major. No special allowances were going to be made, and I assured her that I would not ask for any. I learned to speak very clearly through clenched teeth. Temporarily using a local dentist, my dental visits were scheduled on weekends or after classes. Sticking to my liquid or pureed diet, my weight dropped to slightly below 125 pounds. At five feet ten inches tall, I'm sure everyone thought I looked emaciated, but I loved being that thin. Even though I wanted to eat "normal" food, I couldn't. Opening my mouth even a little bit was tremendously painful, which is also why it took so long to have my teeth repaired.

During a brief visit back home on a weekend, I vividly remember the tears rolling down my cheeks after my mother bought me my favorite grinder sandwich. After attempting one bite, I couldn't eat it due to the pain in my jaw. She felt hurt and unloved when I pushed away the food because she never comprehended what had happened to me. I ended up consoling her instead of the other way around.

Fortunately, classes for the semester ended soon enough. I went back home to work at a full-time, non-medical job through the summer.

There is one unexpected twist to this story. When I moved to Rhode Island several years later, I was employed in an ICU in Providence. While chatting with a respiratory therapist one night, I learned that she is married to a nurse who works at the same Worcester hospital where I did my clinical work and later was also employed. After inquiring what department is his specialty, she notified me that he works in angiography. As the conversation progressed, I learned that he was on duty the day I fainted during the angiography procedure, and that he remembers those events very clearly.

Apparently, ever since that day, whenever any nursing students come for a few hours of procedure observation, they are told about my incident and are forewarned so that nothing like that ever happens again. Not exactly the claim to fame I wanted to embrace. I told her she could pass on the message that I did, indeed, survive nursing school, despite a somewhat rough start.

Life Flight Dreams

I returned home at the completion of my sophomore year, as promised. My preference would have been to work in Worcester as a Student Nurse Intern (SNI) in a hospital, but that wasn't possible. After my father's death, my mother still needed me, and I wanted assurance that she was going to be okay living alone. If I wanted to work in Worcester, I also needed to rent an apartment, and couldn't afford one. At the time, the pay for the SNI jobs was extremely pathetic. The students were making significantly less money than the fast food workers in the city's burger restaurants. I could live at home for free, save some money, and try to get some sort of nursing job next year. Karren agreed to the idea that we could share an apartment next summer if we found something relatively inexpensive in a suitable location.

Working my summer job in the town of Greenfield was one of the best things I could have done that year.

Employed with a lovely bunch of ladies in the tax collector's office at the Town Hall in Greenfield, I worked five days a week, nine to five. I was thankful for this job for many reasons: it helped me pay off student debts, it looked good on a resumé, and it was fairly easy. I didn't directly handle customers and their money, but rather had a variety of simple duties.

Many times, I thought to myself, *This is almost too easy. It's very mundane. If I had to work this job for the remainder of my career, I think I'd go insane. I'm soooo glad I'm in college, training to become a nurse.* It was certainly an eye-opening experience, and very motivational for me to continue with and do well in college. I appreciated the opportunity to work in that job, but when the summer was over, I never worked there again.

School resumed in September, and I continued with my nursing training. Happily, a lot of my clinical practice was based out of the major trauma center in Worcester. The clinicals were challenging and exciting, and I knew the trauma center was where I wanted to work after I graduated. During lunch breaks, I'd sit in the cafeteria and sometimes watch the hospital's helicopter come in for a landing. Arriving back from an accident scene, the life flight nurses would get out in their maroon jumpsuit uniforms and rush the victim to other awaiting staff. *Wow, that's so cool. I want to do THAT.* Watching that helicopter team is what started me on the path toward desiring to be a trauma nurse. I needed a lot of experience, but that was the medical career route I wanted to take.

Mom and Ann at her nursing "pinning" ceremony

A Student Nurse Intern job would help me get my foot in the door for future employment in emergency or trauma medicine as an RN. Karren also wanted paid nursing experience before she graduated. Therefore, we went to Worcester together a couple times during the school year and looked for a place to live so we could work there during the summer. In late spring, we found and leased a nice, little, two-bedroom apartment in the city. I applied and was hired as a SNI on the trauma ward, to be employed over summer vacation. Thankfully, the SNIs were recently given a significant pay raise, which immensely helped with paying the rent. The apartment's location was only five minutes from where I was going to work, and it was also convenient for Karren, who found employment in a different but nearby hospital.

Anyone who has considered nursing as a career

probably realizes that there are endless possibilities associated with this profession. There are many specialties, variable work hours, and the pay can be phenomenal compared to other jobs. Ambitious nurses can become managers, chief nursing officers of hospitals, or pursue further education and become nurse practitioners or professors in higher education institutes. For those individuals who love exploring different regions of the country, travel nursing is always an option. Additionally, you can relocate almost anywhere and easily get hired for a nursing job.

Student Nurse Intern employment was an ideal way to get a little more of a taste of a specialty than what I received during my college education. It was viewed as a temporary job since we were students. If I found out I didn't like or weren't well suited for employment in a particular area, I wouldn't be breaking an expected long-term career commitment. The other positive aspect of the job was that it ranked slightly higher than a nursing assistant. Because a SNI was pursuing a medical career, they were allowed to perform certain procedures that a certified nursing assistant was not. However, neither one was allowed to administer medication or manipulate any intravenous catheter.

At the start of my shift, I would receive an assignment of patients and attended to their needs unless it was something that required the expertise of an actual Registered Nurse. The duties varied, such as obtaining vital signs, performing toileting duties, assisting with mobility, or changing dressings. Often, I provided emotional support to patients, because the RNs were busy performing other duties and simply talking to someone could consume a lot of their time. The clientele on this trauma floor were quite varied and ranged from people approximately my age to geriatric clients. There was always a variety of trauma injuries, although it seemed most of them were from motor vehicle accidents. If a trauma injury was less severe, that individual was probably taken to one of the other nearby hospitals. A few patients in whose care I participated are still vivid in my mind, even after all these years.

One person in particular who stands out is Harley. She was a few years younger than me. Hers was a unique name at the time, and she was as tough as the motorcycle brand with the same name. Harley wanted to live life at lightning speed, but a car accident brought it to a screeching halt. The story was typical of many teenagers: she was out late at night with friends, and the driver was probably speeding on the winding highway that traverses the city of Worcester. She was an unfortunate passenger, although she was wearing her seatbelt, which saved her life. Unlike me when I fractured my jaw, hers was wired shut, and her face was cut up and swollen. Sitting in a hospital bed, she had too much time to think about things. All her frustration was bubbling inside of her, ready to erupt at any moment. Probably the only thing that kept her from throwing something at the wall was the bulky external traction with pins which were holding together the shattered bones of her dominant arm.

Each day I worked, I found Harley's name on my assignment. Caring for her was challenging, mostly because she held on to so much inward anger. I'm sure she didn't enjoy seeing my sunny disposition when she felt so ticked off at the world and her current predicament. Since I wasn't officially an RN yet, I still had a lot to learn about how to converse with patients. It takes time to know how and when to be optimistic, and when to keep your mouth shut and to listen. With Harley, I was starting to figure it out, and always hoped I didn't do or say the wrong thing. Some days with her were okay; others were not.

Eventually, one day I asked that I be given "a break" from taking care of her on my assignment. I needed to spend a shift with different patients so I could mentally regroup, so to speak. Even though I was nowhere close to being "burned out" on this patient, I felt I may be headed that way. I was afraid to make this request, but it was granted. The RNs understood how difficult Harley could be, and they were more sympathetic toward me than I expected.

This did not mean, though, that if they needed help with her, they weren't going to ask me for assistance. Harley needed to go for some routine X-ray, and I was asked to get her into a wheelchair before transport arrived. As I walked into her room and said hello, she seemed very surprised to see me. "I didn't think you were working today" she stated, then continued, "You always take care of me." I felt a little guilty knowing I had made the request to be given a break from her. *Did she actually miss having me as one of her nurses?* It made me stop and think about it.

The following shift that I worked, I asked to resume care for Harley. I guess she wasn't so bad after all. It was a relatively easy workday, and I took care of my duties a little more efficiently than usual. With a bit of spare time on my hands, I asked Harley if she wanted me to wash her hair. It was long, blonde, had some remnants of old, dried blood still in it, and was fairly snarled. She agreed, and we had a unique set up with a specialty-molded basin which allowed me to wash her hair in bed without making a soggy mess. After gently combing out her hair, I was able to French braid it and showed her the results as I held up a mirror. I think that was the first time I saw her genuinely smile—a tremendous grin was on her face.

Not long after that, Harley was well enough to be discharged to home, and I figured I'd never see her again. Surprisingly, I missed her a little bit, because taking care of her had become my routine at work. But our goal as nurses is to help people recover and continue on with their lives. I wasn't working in a long-term care facility. A hospital is a revolving door. One way or another, patients come, and patients go.

About a week or so later, I was walking toward the hospital from the parking garage and heard someone yelling my name. "Ann! Ann!" I turned in the direction of the voice, and saw that it was Harley, leaning out of a car window and wildly waving her arm. Her mother had driven her to the hospital, but I don't know if it was for a follow-up appointment or just to look for me. She called me over because she had something she wanted to give me: a handwritten note. Harley excitedly told me that she decided that she wanted to become a nurse and was going to apply to nursing school in the future. It was the care I provided to her that inspired her to make this life choice. She got out of the car for a few moments, gave me the note and a huge hug, then waved goodbye.

Who could have predicted that someone like me, who wasn't even an RN yet, could make that kind of impact on another individual's life? Her return was timely, and solidified my determination to be the best nurse I am capable of being. I hope I never forget the words she said and wrote to me. She was kind and thankful, and I was immensely happy for her promising future. I think I still have that note stashed away somewhere in my belongings.

Harley returned to the hospital and told me about the impact I made in her life. Perhaps there were other patients or their family members who felt the same way? I'll never know the answer to that question.

Thank you, Harley. I hope you became a nurse. You probably affected my life almost as much as I influenced yours.

Jump Back

It seems every generation of nurses has to contend with some sort of newly discovered disease or illness. In the year 2020, nurses were taking care of patients with COVID-19. As I write this, they are continuing to take care of patients who develop that disease, although probably there are not as many of them today. Without a doubt, life was difficult for new nurses who were hired in an overburdened hospital, required to take care of so many extremely sick patients, especially in the ICUs. Even the experienced nurses, in any department, may have been told to take care of someone with COVID-19. Stress levels were very high everywhere.

A different infection was plaguing the country, and other parts of the world, when I was starting my nursing education and career in the late 1980s. The diseases were called "HIV" and "AIDS." It appeared very little was known about these viruses by most people. There were more questions about them than proven facts. Somewhere, I'm sure, there were highly educated doctors and scientists who had a lot of knowledge about those diseases, but that was not the norm.

My first encounter with a patient who was diagnosed with HIV occurred when I worked on the trauma ward. I clearly remember a big placard placed on the entrance to his room, warning staff and visitors about required isolation. A cart filled with protective gear, including gowns, gloves, and face shields, was parked outside of the room, as well. If hazmat suits were available, I'm sure the nurses and doctors would have been wearing them in order to protect themselves from this patient.

I'm only speaking for myself when I say that this patient scared me. He wasn't physically or verbally intimidating. Rather, it was his disease that frightened me. HIV is spread via a person's blood, but no one was 100 percent positive that it wasn't spread through saliva or urine. Could the disease have a respiratory component? Will I get sick if he coughed on me? Although I tried to remain calm and cordial whenever I had to enter his room, I performed my duties as an SNI quickly in order to minimize time in there.

More than physical isolation, I'm sure the patient felt emotionally or socially isolated, as well. Remember, this was the 80s, and most people did not have cell phones. Nurses didn't linger long in his room, and he was not permitted to walk freely up and down the hallways.

We, and most hospitals, probably made similar mistakes in that decade. So much has been learned about HIV and AIDS since that era, and more effective medications have been developed. Patients are living much longer with those diseases, which were once considered an absolute death sentence for many people.

Our HIV patient wasn't on our ward because of trauma. Most of us probably felt relief when it was time for him to be discharged to home. On the day of his discharge, he was brought to the nurses' station in a wheelchair. It was required that a patient is actually wheeled to the exit of the hospital or to the curb, even if they are capable of ambulating.

I was walking down the hallway toward the nurses' station when I saw this patient stand up and step away from the wheelchair. Completely without warning, he unzipped his pants and proceeded to pee directly onto the desk area wall, and all over the floor. He didn't care if anyone was in the immediate vicinity, he would have sprayed them, too. Almost simultaneously, everyone jumped back. He must have drunk a gallon of water in order to urinate that much.

He was angry and wanted to intentionally scare or harm us because of his perceived mistreatment. Spending his entire hospitalization solely in his hospital room, he probably sensed our desire to keep our distance from him. Although he was not a prisoner, he probably felt we treated him like one because he was not allowed to leave that room until the day he left.

Perhaps his actions could be considered assault,

but no one retaliated against him or considered suing. Nurses are tolerant of other people's behavior and are sympathetic to the range of emotions patients feel. Nurses don't deserve to be abused in any manner by patients or their families, but most of us understand why it happens.

We care about people, and I hope that is one thing that never changes in the nursing profession.

East vs. West

In all the years I have been a nurse, I never regretted going to a four-year college and earning my Bachelor of Science in Nursing degree. I had briefly considered applying to a nursing diploma program, which is a three-year program. An associate degree in nursing involved going to college for two years, which is something I did not want to do. My reasons for the choice were simple: I knew that if I wanted to advance my career in the future, I would eventually have to earn a BSN degree. Achieving it while I was young was the easiest and most desirable path for me. Also, I wanted to play competitive tennis. I knew FSC had a tennis team, but the diploma schools probably only focused on academics.

Cost was also a factor when I applied to schools, as well as the logistics of traveling back and forth from home. An in-state college was reasonably priced, and I didn't amass a large amount of debt. I've worked with nurses who went to more elite schools for their nursing degrees which were more expensive than FSC. Did that matter when it came to pay? No, it did not. We all made the same amount of pay, based on our seniority at our jobs. Nursing students may go to a school with a prettier campus, or which has a more prestigious reputation, but in the end, we're all RNs. Hopefully those nurses had an enjoyable college campus experience to make it worth what they or their parents had to pay for that education. A student should pick a college or school which works best for their own circumstances or desires. Even if I had more financial resources, I don't think I would have made a different college decision.

FSC was also centrally located in Massachusetts. If I had applied to nearby UMass in Amherst, which my parents wanted me to attend, they would have insisted that I live at home. I was determined to break away from home and finally gain some independence as an adult, so going away to school was something I felt compelled to do. When I was a sophomore and my father died, commuting back and forth to home for a short period of time was a bit of a hassle. But if I lived at home, there would be a lot of distractions, similar to when I was in high school. My parents had no idea the amount of work involved in being a good student and maintaining a sufficient grade point average. I had made the best choice possible for myself.

There was one large drawback, however, to attending a four-year school. When I started college, there was a

FSC Nursing class of 1989 (Ann in top row)

great demand for nurses in almost every specialty. I was thrilled knowing that it wouldn't be difficult obtaining a job after graduation. But over the course of the next few years, things dramatically changed. There was a large influx of nurses entering the profession. Many of them, seeking to obtain jobs quickly, went to those two or three-year nursing programs previously mentioned. They became nurses more quickly than me and filled jobs I had been eyeing.

Fortunately for me, I was working as a Student Nurse Intern in the hospital where I wanted to be employed after graduation. I was told that I would be guaranteed a job, but it was not going to be on the trauma ward. I was given the choice of picking employment on either a cardiac or neurology ward; both those jobs were only available on the night shift. Since I was never fond of studying neurology issues in school, I chose the cardiac floor. Little did I know that cardiovascular patients would become my specialty in the future, with an emphasis in critical care. Indeed, the "drawback" of not obtaining a trauma job was actually a blessing in disguise, and it altered the course of my nursing career. I transitioned from the east side of the third floor to the west side, and worked there until I relocated to Rhode Island in 1991.

Does Anyone
Have a Shovel?

On a warm summer evening, I never would have guessed I'd need a shovel going to work. No, not a snow shovel—I needed something completely different.

I was getting used to working the night shift, and actually I enjoyed working on the cardiovascular surgical floor. There was so much to learn which college didn't teach me, and I soaked it up like a sponge. It was hard work, but with experience I hoped things would get easier for me. Organizing your time and setting your priorities plays a big role in the nursing profession, but people and healthcare situations are unpredictable at times, and unexpected things can happen.

The busiest times of my shift were usually the start and the end. Making my first rounds allowed me to meet my clients and gauge how to set my priorities. It also gave me an idea of what kind of night may be in store for me. The end of the shift was equally busy, for different reasons. A couple of my patients were often pre-operative for open heart surgery, and if they were the first cases on the schedule, they needed to be ready to be rolled to the OR. Most patients had medications due at six o'clock in the morning, which was shortly before my night was over. There were also other expectations, such as changing dressings, unwrapping leg ace wraps, and replacing wraps with anti-embolic stockings. I also assisted patients with mobility to the bathroom instead of providing a quicker solution in the form of a bedside commode. They needed to walk and return to normal functioning in preparation for going home.

On this particular morning, I helped a pleasant gentleman shuffle to the bathroom. He moved slowly, but that was not unexpected. After sitting him on the toilet seat, I told him to pull the emergency light when he was done. And above all, DON'T FLUSH THE TOILET. We needed to witness that someone actually had a bowel movement; it was a requirement before someone could be discharged from the hospital. Some patients were embarrassed by this, but it ensured that they would not have problems when they went home if they lied about using the toilet when they actually didn't.

I closed the door for some privacy, but I usually didn't stray too far from a room while waiting for someone on a toilet. There was always a little charting I could complete, or I could prepare to administer medication to the patient's roommate.

It wasn't long before I saw the bathroom warning light flash, indicating that my patient had completed his mission and was ready to be assisted back to his bedside chair. After opening the door, I helped him to his feet, making sure he was steady before attempting the walk back to his side of the hospital room. What I saw next left me totally speechless. Next to the toilet, on the floor, was the biggest pile of human poop I had ever seen. It looked like something that could have been produced by a Clydesdale horse—it was enormous. *How did that happen?* I thought I had him seated directly over the toilet bowl. He was a rather large man; he must have somehow shifted his weight to one side without realizing he was no longer properly sitting on the toilet seat. It's impossible to imagine how that much poop *completely* missed the inside of the toilet.

I doubt this gentleman knew what he had just done. He was facing forward, and I said nothing regarding the mess that I was going to have to clean up. I walked him back toward his recliner, believing that this mellow patient didn't intentionally shit on the floor in order to give me a vindictive goodbye gift. But the fact remained that I couldn't leave this massive pile of poo on the ground. As much as I wanted to, I couldn't ask a housekeeper to clean it up, either. I grabbed a few towels off the linen cart and tried to scoop it up without dropping it onto my shoes or clothing. Then, I retrieved a few more towels from the cart. Maybe a bed sheet would have worked better? No. I needed a shovel. But unfortunately, I didn't have one. Perhaps twenty minutes later, the bathroom floor was fairly clean.

After my shift ended, I went home and took a long, hot, disinfecting shower. Thankfully, nothing like that ever happened again during my career.

Fever

A few weeks after I took care of the gentleman who pooped on the floor, I had a pre-op patient who was assigned to the same room. I'm very fortunate to have had the opportunity to take care of so many wonderful patients. This particular gentleman was no exception. Despite facing his upcoming surgery later in the day, he was full of good humor and optimism, and it was a pleasure taking care of him.

While preparing to wrap up my night, I received a call from the OR that my patient was going to be moved from second to first case of the day. Apparently, the patient who was the first operative case had spiked a fever during the night, so the surgeon refused to operate on him that day. The doctor was not going to take a chance on performing an elective procedure on someone who may have an active infection.

I informed my patient of the news, and his reaction

was mixed. He was glad to not have to wait around all day and think about the upcoming surgery, so it was good news. However, his family wasn't planning on driving to the hospital until later that morning, so he probably wouldn't get to see them again before he was taken to the OR. They lived approximately an hour away, and receiving this notice at the last minute would not enable them to get to the hospital in time to personally wish him well—especially considering Worcester traffic during rush hour. Nonetheless, I told him I would inform them of the change and called them from the nurses' station. I located a portable phone and brought it to his room so he could call them and chat for a few minutes. Hearing each other's voices would probably provide them with some comfort.

You have to remember that back in the 80s and early 90s, nobody had a smartphone. Very few ordinary citizens had any type of portable phone, and there was definitely no Facetime available. Individual patients didn't have landlines in their rooms, which was good in a way, because it allowed them to get the rest they needed while in the hospital.

After he hung up the phone and I helped him onto the stretcher, I told him I'd check with the ICU that night to see how things went during the surgery. In a couple days or less, he'd be back on "3-West," and I'd probably take care of him again before he went home. After saying our goodbyes, I went home to sleep before returning back for another shift that night.

Upon arriving back to work that evening, I checked

with the cardiac surgical assistant to get an update on my patient from that morning. Sadly, he informed me that he died in the OR. I didn't ask for details, because they didn't matter since he didn't survive. I asked one of the day shift nurses if his family made it to the hospital in time to see him once more; she told me that they were too late. I should have known the outcome wasn't good. Usually, I see a multitude of family members crammed into the waiting room outside of the cardiac surgical ICU, which is near the stairwell that I utilize to get to the third floor. I had met his lovely family the previous evening, and they weren't among the people in that room.

It's unbelievable how you can grow to care about someone in a short span of twelve hours. But that's what sometimes happens to nurses. It truly is a caring profession, and most nurses have an abundance of empathy for their patients. I'm glad I arrived early to work that night, because I had time to go into the bathroom for a few minutes to privately cry. Rest in peace, dear patient.

Welcome to Rhode Island

A lot of extremely cute young doctors either worked at or were going through their residency programs where I worked in Massachusetts. Being somewhat shy and not very skilled at flirting with men, I never dated any of them. I know my mother was always hoping I would meet and marry a doctor, but there was probably little chance of that happening. Sometimes I think elderly parents like mine feel that's the primary reason to become a nurse. It's a fairly unrealistic expectation. If they knew the long or difficult hours some doctors work, and the debt they incur because of their medical education, parents would probably not think having a doctor for a spouse is such a grand idea. It all depends on the individual person and specialty; not all physician careers are alike.

The person whom I started dating was not in the medical profession, and he lived in Rhode Island. Commuting back and forth between where we lived in order to see each other was not easy, and the drive was becoming downright tedious after only six months. I was starting to do the majority of the driving, spending most of my free time at his house, since it was much nicer than where I lived. Finally, the decision was made that I'd move to Rhode Island and get a new job at one of the local hospitals.

After applying to both a large trauma center as well as a smaller community hospital, I was offered jobs at both hospitals. I chose the smaller hospital because their human resource department was the one which contacted me first, and I began making plans to relocate. During the process of moving, I was once again contacted by an employee from human resources. She stated that after reviewing my job application, they felt my skills were more appropriate for a new unit that was being built. Construction of that unit was just starting, and it was going to be a "step-down" unit called CVT-I.

CVT meant cardiovascular thoracic, and the "I" signified "intermediate." The purpose of this unit was to care for patients who no longer required ICU-level care, but who needed more attention than could be given on a standard ward. Its primary function was to be an extension of care provided to the cardiothoracic post-op patients. Eventually, the area would be utilized to care for a more diverse variety of intermediate level patients.

In the meantime, if I wanted the job, I would be

trained in ICU and then transition to the new step-down unit when it opened. It sounded like a fantastic opportunity, so I agreed to that plan.

As I was trained in the ICU, I began to know the nurses and liked working with most of them. After my orientation period on day shift was over, I was employed as a full-time nurse on the night shift. I enjoyed where I was working, so I was dreading having to leave that group of people in order to start the job for which I was hired on the second floor. However, construction delays persisted, and several more months went by before CVT-I was ready to open.

It was difficult to imagine that an entire year had passed since the time I was initially hired. I had strictly worked in the ICU throughout that time, and I didn't want to leave that staff and work with different people in CVT-I. Unbelievably, one morning my current manager approached me and wanted to speak with me in her office. She inquired if I felt comfortable working in the ICU and if I wanted to continue employment there instead of moving up to the second floor. Without hesitation, I informed her I wanted to stay in the ICU. Being given the choice of where I preferred to work made me extremely happy. I think a few of my colleagues on nights were also glad I made that decision. Our personalities worked well together, and they didn't want to have to go through the process of training someone new again.

Thus began my life as an ICU nurse. Circumstances fell into place which allowed me to specialize in critical care, and it shaped the future course of my career.

Boxers or Briefs?

During my orientation months, I worked on the day shift, usually with one primary preceptor. However, she had days off and took a summer vacation, so other nurses shared those duties. I enjoyed being trained by the various other nurses. Everyone had their own style and described or explained things in their own way. I was assured that with time I'd also develop my unique style after learning what works best for me. Being precepted by a diversity of nurses allowed me to take the best of what I observed and create my own habits.

On this particular day, I was shadowing Darby. She took good care of her patients and it was easy working with her. She had a terrific sense of humor and was known as a prankster. Although she hadn't pulled any jokes on me yet, I knew I would eventually be the victim of one of her creative and witty schemes. Today however, her attention was focused on someone else.

During the current month, there was a particular Resident doctor who everyone noticed. He was rather handsome, but that's not what caught our attention. It was mostly unspoken among us, but we were all aware of the thin nature of his scrub pants. Fortunately, he was wearing underwear beneath his scrubs, but that's where the fun part begins. His underwear was always boxer shorts, and through the threadbare scrubs, we could easily distinguish the pattern of the day. The design could be anything—such as stars, dogs, stripes, or polka dots. Heck, at least we knew he changed his underwear every day.

Today, however, those boxer shorts won the prize. The underwear consisted of a daisy flower pattern, and Darby and I held back chuckles when he arrived in the ICU. He informed us that he needed to insert an arterial line catheter into our patient's wrist, as instructed by the ICU director. We gathered the materials necessary for the procedure, set up a few items in advance, and were ready to assist him and start in a few minutes. With a wide, mischievous grin on her face, Darby turned to me and said, "Watch this…"

She took a couple of spare, new, round electrocardiogram (ECG) leads, and began drawing big flower petals around the center point on them that resembled the flowers on the Resident's shorts. Peeling away the protective backing, she attached the sticky ECG leads to her dress, one over each breast. Then she put her scrub jacket back on for a brief duration. After the Resident returned and was starting the procedure, she made a calculated comment, saying, "Wow, it's really hot in here." She took off her jacket and hung it on a nearby IV pole. Without drawing any attention to herself, she waited for the Resident to notice how she had embellished the top of her scrub dress. Since he was completely focused on procedural technique, it was several minutes before he looked up at the cardiac monitor to see if the catheter was placed properly, achieving an acceptable waveform. Standing beside the monitor was Darby, who was looking calmly off into the distance. The Resident *finally* noticed the daisy flowers stuck to her chest. I don't think I've ever seen anyone turn so instantly and completely that shade of red in the face. After finishing up with the procedure, he made a quick exit and Darby removed any evidence of her prank.

To us, it was good-natured fun, and we meant no harm. We had a hearty laugh, and he was a good sport about the whole thing. I doubt she could get away with doing something like that in this current era, because too many people are uptight and quick to shout, "lateral violence" or, "sexism." Yes, those things do exist in the workplace, but she meant no ill will, and certainly would have apologized to him if he was offended by the prank. We learned that his girlfriend was the one who bought him all those boxers because she thought they were cute, and he did begin wearing slightly thicker scrub pants.

Sundowning

Working the night shift—whether it is 7 p.m. to 7:30 a.m. or 11 p.m. to 7:30 a.m., brings its own unique challenges. Despite what many people want to believe, nurses aren't allowed to sleep at night, and it's not an easier or quieter shift. It is a very interesting shift, and I learned to love it. Every time a day shift job was available, I passed it by, preferring to work nights "just a little while longer."

Still being what some may consider a "new nurse," I was frequently learning things about the medical profession and the night shift itself. Take, for instance, what I learned about the sweet little Grandma I was caring for on a routine night.

My female patient was a pleasant elderly woman. I would have loved to have adopted her as my own Grandma. All my grandparents were deceased before I was born, so I never knew any of them. The start of my shift with her was excellent. We chatted about various things, and it was a pleasure caring for her. I dimmed the lights and provided a relaxing environment so she could obtain much-needed rest.

Not long after the time I left the patient, perhaps an hour or so, I heard strange sounds coming from her room. I investigated what was happening, and I found her in a strange position in the bed. The noises were coming from the rattling and kicking of the bedrails, reminiscent of an angry animal banging on the bars of a cage. *Good grief. What is the problem in here?* She wouldn't tell me about her problem; she simply looked at me as if I was evil. In truth, *she* was the one who appeared demonic. It was as if someone had flipped a switch, and my adorable Grandma turned into a character from a Halloween horror movie. She was crazy and resisted any effort I made to assist her or speak calmly with her. I couldn't understand what was happening to her.

The Intern and Resident who were overseeing her care were useless. They couldn't rationalize with her either, and they didn't want to prescribe any medication to calm this elderly patient. Eventually, I received an order for a miniscule dose of sedative. She looked at me suspiciously as I prepared to administer the medication to her.

With narrowed eyes and a hoarse voice from all her yelling, she squinted at me and said, "So, you think you're going to drug me? If I fall and break a hip, I'm going to *sue you* for everything you own!"

Gail

Oh, the situation was getting better with each passing moment, wasn't it? I ended up being sequestered in the room with her all night. She kept trying to get out of bed without assistance and escape. It was as if she intentionally wanted to break her hip, to spite herself and cause trouble for me.

When morning thankfully arrived, my efforts to obtain blood from her were futile, because she wouldn't let me touch her.

"Keep your dirty hands away from me or I'll scream!" she exclaimed.

Out of desperation, I enlisted the help of my colleague Gail. Since she had once taken care of oncology patients, she was very skilled at phlebotomy. I practically bribed her to help me. She went into the patient's room and introduced herself as I watched from a safe distance through a glass window. Pulling up a chair, she looked at the woman's arm and quickly and easily drew her blood. I saw the woman patting Gail's hand, telling her she was a fine nurse, asking her to come back and visit anytime. As Gail walked out of the room, handing me the vials of blood, she had a smirk on her face.

"She wouldn't let me go anywhere near her," I said. "How did you do that?"

Gail jokingly made a remark regarding how fabulous she is with patients, how everyone loves her.

Actually, it was something else altogether. My patient had gone through "Sundowning" syndrome. It's a phenomenon which is described as occurring when an elderly person starts becoming confused in the evening, such as when the sun is going down. When daylight occurs, the person's mentation begins to clear, and they act like their usual self again. Gail knew what was happening and waited a little while before attempting to draw her blood. She knew the patient would be more amiable near the end of our shift.

Lesson learned: sundowning is a real issue. I learned to not take personally any negative comments many of my older patients said to me at night.

Get the Air Spray

Most people are aware that nurses encounter quite a variety of bodily fluids from their patients. Any orifice that produces something that can be expelled has been managed by a nurse at one time or another. If you're a person who is squeamish about cleaning, suctioning, or sticking tubes into any opening in the human body, the nursing profession is probably not the career choice you want to make.

Fortunately, not many things emanating from a patient disgust me. I accept managing waste products as part of the job. But to be totally honest, my least favorite activity is probably emptying a colostomy bag. Although colostomy bags are made of disposable plastic, a nurse still has to empty its fecal contents at the end of the shift and document the quantity. This measurement, which occurred every eight hours, was part of a patient's overall daily intake and output assessment. There's just something different about draining a colostomy container versus cleaning a patient who has had explosive diarrhea in the bed. It's one of the quirky little things that I dislike. Everyone has something they'd rather not do on the job, and I've told my secret.

On one particular night, I cared for a patient who had a colostomy, and it was time for me to empty the collection bag contents. With the curtains in the patient's room pulled together for privacy, I began draining the bag. What resembled loose, brown, bubbling lava flowed into the plastic measuring cylinder. Something about the nutrition my patient was receiving didn't agree with him, or perhaps the antibiotics were causing his gastric distress. Regardless, the smell was making my eyes water, and I was gagging. The wastebasket beside the bed was looking like a potential target for the vomit that was about to come spewing from my own mouth.

Thinking perhaps that I was being overly sensitive, my fears were soon put to rest. I heard several of my colleagues outside of the room saying things such as, "Ughhhh," "Oh, that's so gross," "I'm gonna puke," "Get the air spray," and, "*Where* is that coming from?" On and on, the comments continued. Hey, they should have smelled it from my location.

I couldn't get rid of the cylinder of poop fast enough. Unfortunately, in our old ICU—which was built in the 1960s—several rooms shared one big flush toilet in the dirty utility room. I had to carry the container past a couple rooms in order to dump the waste.

When I walked past my colleague, Gail, and she saw what was in my hands, she burst out into hysterical laughter. *Sure, Gail, it's really funny. You have your clean cardiac surgical patient, and I have my stinky gastric disaster.* I said nothing to her, not wanting to delay my mission of emptying the malodorous contents I was holding.

Upon returning to my patient's bedside, I continued finishing up my duties prior to the end of the shift. Gail came over to where I was standing and let me know there was something she had to tell me.

She was still chuckling a little bit when she said, "I didn't know what you were doing in the room because you had the curtains closed. I was squatting down, measuring the levels on the Pleur-evac when I let loose a little silent-but-deadly fart. I didn't think it was going to stink so much. When I saw you walking out with the poop container, I was relieved the smell wasn't from me."

She honestly thought everyone was gagging from her flatulence and was embarrassed to admit what she had done. I started laughing, too, and wished I had seen the look on her face when everyone else was making the "Get the air spray" comments.

Bag and Tag

When taking care of the sickest patients in the hospital, it is not unexpected that some of them will die in ICU. Each nurse dealt with death of a patient in his or her own way. Most of us developed some sort of self-protective mechanism to deal with the emotions we felt. Until you work in what may be considered a stressful environment and witness occasional or frequent deaths, you may never understand nurses' sense of humor. I don't believe the general public would probably agree with the things that we may deem as funny.

Unlike Darby, I'm not a prankster, but I do have a very dry sense of humor at times. I almost never play jokes on people, but maybe that is why I'm successful when I do try to fool someone. It was my turn to trick a person, and Gail was the target.

On that night, Gail's patient died, and that in itself

was not the least bit funny. Mr. Scalo's health had been declining steadily over several days. With his advanced age, it was not likely he would have survived much longer. His family, including his beloved wife, made the decision to make him Do Not Resuscitate (DNR) status. They were given the option of staying at his bedside as long as they wanted, but no one could predict with certainty how long it would take him to pass away. He might die hours or days from now. Since his wife was quite aged herself, the family took her home to prevent her from also becoming ill or exhausted.

The gentleman died peacefully with nurses at his side. The only fortunate thing about the situation is that we were not the ones who had to notify the family of his death. That was the MD's responsibility, and they were also the ones who called the medical examiner to see if an autopsy was necessary. Before the doctor called the patient's wife, we told him to ask if she was going to return to the hospital to see him one more time. The answer was to the effect of, "Possibly, but not likely." We discussed her response among ourselves. Whether or not she was going to come back to the hospital affected what we did next. We needed to start post-mortem care. If Mrs. Scalo desired to see him again in the hospital, we would try to make him look as serene as possible, place chairs near the bedside, and remove extraneous medical devices from the room. If she didn't want to see him until he arrived at the funeral home, we'd perform all the necessary post-mortem responsibilities before he was taken to the morgue.

A few duties which were routinely completed while preparing someone for the morgue included disconnecting all medical equipment from the patient. We washed the person one last time after we removed all IVs and tubes from the body. The only time the IVs and tubes weren't removed was if an autopsy was required. The body was wrapped in a plastic sheet and placed in a large bag after identification tags were attached. Finally, we double checked the patient's room and collected any personal belongings and placed them in a second labeled bag which would remain with the deceased person.

Considering Mrs. Scalo's age and frail status, we agreed that she probably would not return to the hospital in the middle of the night. A Transport staff member retrieved a gurney for us and told us to call him back when we completed what we needed to do. We respectfully prepared the body to be stored in the morgue and waited for the return of the Transport personnel.

Not having had a break in a while, we all decided to sit down for a few minutes before our next round of patient vital signs and medications were required. I wanted to take a quick run to the vending machines for a cold soda, so I excused myself from the unit. On the way back to the ICU, I had to pass by the waiting room. It was at that time that I decided to pull my prank on Gail.

As was standard protocol, anyone wishing to visit someone in the ICU had to call from the waiting room phone and request permission before entering. I picked up the phone and dialed our extension.

"Good morning, this is ICU, how may I help you?" stated a voice which I recognized.

"May I speak to Mr. Scalo's nurse, please?" I inquired in a disguised creaky voice, trying to sound like an elderly woman.

"Who's calling, please?" my colleague asked.

I lied, saying, "This is Mrs. Scalo. I couldn't go back to sleep after the phone call, so I contacted my daughter and she brought me back to the hospital."

Silence. I imagined the looks of panic on the nurses' faces as they sat around the main table near the telephone.

"Just one moment, Mrs. Scalo, we'll get the nurse for you."

After what seemed like an eternity, Gail finally picked up the phone. I bet the long delay was because they were trying to figure out what to tell me, or what to do, since the patient's body was already neatly wrapped, bagged, and tagged.

Gail started saying, "Mrs. Scalo..."

However, I couldn't let her continue. I was laughing so hard it truly sounded like I was crying, but I confessed that it was me, Ann. Then I laughed even harder as I listened to the colorful language Gail used to tell me what she thought of my deception. After walking down the short hall to the ICU and rejoining my crew, I found they were stunned I managed to pull off that prank. Indeed, they were a bit panicked over what they should do, and were really relieved it was just a joke.

I've occasionally thought about whether that trick

was in poor taste or not, and I never did anything like that in the future. I was not meaning any disrespect toward the patient or his family; I just wanted to break up the tension of the night. In addition, we all learned an important lesson that shift: if one of our patients dies, we better make darn sure no family is coming back to the hospital for a final goodbye.

I'll Never Wear THAT Again

Safety is always one of the top priorities in a hospital. I'm referring to patient safety, although keeping staff safe is also extremely important. One of the worst things that can happen to a patient is if they fall, whether it's out of bed or a chair, or while ambulating. It is our duty to make sure patients don't get injured in any manner. I certainly know I would never want to be the cause of someone's broken hip due to negligence. Accidents occasionally do happen despite vigilance, but we definitely do try to avoid any mishaps while a patient is under our care.

I was taking care of an older gentleman who was in the ICU because he needed to be on a ventilator while receiving treatment for his current medical issues. His pulmonary condition was chronic, and he already had a tracheostomy that was required years ago. Being a frail and thin man, we had him on a special air mattress to prevent skin breakdown, known as decubiti. Those mattresses, although they protected skin over bony prominences by reducing pressure on the body, were somewhat slippery. Since they were designed to also minimize friction on skin, the patients easily slid around on them.

Sitting with my colleagues at our central ICU table, I was completing some charting. We could see most of the patients' rooms from that location, as well as the cardiac monitors. With the lights dimmed to promote sleep, sometimes it was a little difficult to see when the patients were being mischievous. The patients who warranted being watched closely were checked very frequently, or a nurse stayed in the room most of the time. My patient was well behaved, or so I thought.

Upon hearing a ventilator alarm signal coming from my patient's room, I immediately got up and went to investigate the matter. The man for whom I was caring had disconnected the ventilator tubing from his trach and looked like he was going to start sliding out of the bed. His legs were hanging slightly over the edge of the bed; I rushed to his side upon seeing his position. Swiftly grabbing the vent tubing and reattaching it to his trach, I simultaneously maneuvered myself to prevent him from slipping out of the bed. Knowing that his breathing was okay, I put a hand on either side of his body and sat him upright. We were face to face in the mostly dark room. I did not want to let go of him at the moment, and I couldn't reach the call light to ask for assistance. Knowing that other nearby patients were sleeping, and that my own patient wasn't in imminent danger, I thought that yelling "HELP!" loud enough to grab someone's attention was inappropriate. I'd give him a minute to get reoriented to his surroundings, then I'd gently lay him back down in bed while swinging his legs into it as well.

While I was waiting a minute to catch my own breath after running into the room, my patient made his next move. He had been holding onto my shoulders for balance; he slowly reached toward my neck. I wasn't fearing he was going to choke me, but I didn't predict what he was going to do next. With an enormous grin on his face, he put his hand on the zipper of my shirt and pulled it down as far as it would go. Fortunately, it wasn't a full-length zipper, but his actions did expose a lot of skin and my boobs. *What a dirty old man.* He thought it was amusing. *No, I'm not here in the dark with you for THAT reason. I'm your nurse, and now you're getting placed back into bed with only yourself for company.* After promptly rezipping my shirt, I was finally able to get someone's attention, and the patient was properly reposition for safety.

While looking at that old cotton shirt in the laundry basket after I got home, I decided that it had seen more than its share of action in the ICU. It was one of my favorites, but it was getting worn out and needed to be retired. After that, I started wearing scrub tops that didn't utilize any tempting zippers.

No, no charges of sexual harassment or anything else were ever brought against this man, who was, more than anything, just confused. His actions were the least of my concerns during my span of employment as a nurse; I considered them fairly harmless.

Nurses take a lot more significant abuse over the course of their careers, mine included, compared to a shirt which was unzipped. I know I'm not alone when I say patients going through drug or alcohol withdrawal have sworn at or tried to intimidate me. I've been spit at or roughly pinched on whatever area of my body that a patient could reach. Once in a great while, someone tried to strangle me with the stethoscope which hung around my own neck. I even had one patient attempt to kick me in the head while I was obtaining a measurement from one of his drainage tubes hanging on the side of his bed. Fortunately, I had fast reaction times during those patient behaviors and always escaped serious injury.

Most of those actions were attributed to a patient's dementia, ICU psychosis, waking up from anesthesia medication, or substance withdrawal. Occasionally, there is no excuse for a patient's behavior—they're just naturally mean or angry individuals. Overall, people simply are not at their best when they're ill and in the hospital. It's something nurses accept and endure as part of the job. Besides helping patients become well, that's one of the biggest reasons nurses should be appreciated and thanked.

Christmas

One of the things that may influence someone's decision on whether or not to become a nurse is the fact that we have to work weekends and holidays. Many people forget that a hospital is open 24/7, every day of the year. Sure, some times of the year—in certain departments—may be "slower" during the holidays, when surgeons want to take vacations or time off to be with their families. But even when elective surgeries are delayed until after the holidays, unpredicted emergencies occur—and flu season cases especially influence the census levels.

Various hospitals have different ways of determining which holiday a nurse is going to work. Usually, it is some sort of alternating method, but staff seniority may also be a factor. In the ICU where I worked, every other holiday was worked by an individual. On the "major holidays," such as Fourth of July or Christmas, you definitely worked whichever one you did not work the previous year. Fortunately, among ourselves, we could trade shifts with other staff members. For example, some of the older nurses didn't go out to party on New Year's Eve. They'd happily work those nights in exchange for having Thanksgiving off, since they had many family members and a big feast at their house each year. You get the idea.

My personal preference was having Christmas Eve off. There was always something special about that night for me, ever since I was a child. I loved the glow of the Christmas tree lights and candles; seasonal music; and all the anticipation leading up to Christmas day. Once Christmas Day arrived, it was all over for me, because I didn't have small children or copious relatives I needed to visit. However, this year, I couldn't find anyone who wanted to work Christmas Eve for me.

Most people didn't complain about working the holiday—it is what it is. We made the best of the situation, and usually everyone brought in something special to eat to make the atmosphere more festive. Some of us wore brightly colored clothes or unique jewelry or headpieces in an effort to be cheerful and show holiday spirit to our patients, their families, and each other. I usually stuck to traditional red or green scrubs, and had cute dangling earrings. Sometimes I remembered to attach a Christmas pin to my scrub top.

The patient on my assignment this Christmas Eve was a young man named John who was admitted to the hospital about a week ago. I consistently took care of him from the first day he arrived in ICU. His mother was a wonderful woman who cared deeply for her son, and it broke her heart to see him in the ICU. My heart was filled with much empathy for her, which was compounded by the fact that he was so young and it was the holiday season.

John was a college student and had just returned home for winter break after completing his final exams. Happy to be back home, he wanted to be reunited with his friends whom he had not seen since last summer, before he started college. John, who was about twenty years old, stayed out late one night with those friends, then came home and went to bed. Knowing he was out until the early hours of the morning, John's mother let him sleep in late, guessing that he was probably pretty tired. When it was almost noontime, she finally knocked on his bedroom door, ready to drag him out of bed. After knocking several times and receiving no answer, she opened his door to check on him, and found him unconscious. Unable to wake him, she immediately called 911 for help.

An insulin-dependent diabetic, John's blood sugar was abnormally low, and he was in a coma. Appropriate measures were taken by the EMTs, such as checking his blood sugar and administering dextrose. Since he remained unresponsive, he was intubated for airway safety and transferred to our ICU for continued care.

Despite normalization of all of his bloodwork values and brain scans, John didn't wake up. It didn't make sense. There was no reason why he wasn't awake.

Each evening his mother came to visit after she completed her workday. She sat at John's bedside, hoping and praying for him to get better and open his eyes. But he made no movement whatsoever, and after almost a week, the situation was looking pretty grim.

On Christmas Eve, she was once again sitting at his bedside with tears in her eyes. I gave her a hug when she decided to go home for the night, promising to take good care of her son, and telling her that I'd be off from work the following night.

I took care of John and my other patient the way I always did. Since it was now early Christmas morning, each of the staff went about washing their patients and trying to make them look as good as possible, considering there would probably be many visitors today in the ICU. We shaved the faces of people who were usually clean shaven, combed hair so it looked neat, and made sure bed linens were clean. Those were the few visible things we could do to bring comfort to the families. Usually, we started what we call "a.m. care" around four o'clock in the morning, after bloodwork was drawn and vital signs were documented. Routinely, we turned on one of the communal TVs as a little bit of background distraction. Most of our patients were intubated, so our conversations with them were primarily one-sided. I always talked to my patients, even though they couldn't audibly reply. I also talked to them if they were heavily sedated, or in a coma, such as young John. One of the nurses found a channel which was replaying the Pope's Midnight Mass from the Vatican. The mass was probably originally aired much earlier due to the time zone differences, so I was happy to have an opportunity to watch it. No one objected to having the TV on, and we proceeded with our work.

Working as a team, we helped each other with personal care of the patients. It's almost impossible to turn a patient side-to-side in bed by yourself. If a patient is intubated, it's too risky to even consider doing something like that for fear of accidental extubation. A couple of my colleagues came over to John's bedside to help me reposition him and change his bed linen. When we completed this task, we couldn't believe what we were seeing. John was opening his eyes, and starting to move his arms. *He's awake. He's awake!* Clearly, he wasn't aware of his surroundings, and he was trying to pull at the tube in his mouth, unable to understand what it was and why it was there.

I started talking to him, saying something such as, "John, you're in the ICU in the hospital. You've been really sick because your blood sugar was too low. That's a breathing tube in your mouth; don't pull at it. You'll hurt yourself. We're going to try to take it out." He actually nodded his head in response and was able to squeeze my hands when I asked him to follow some of my commands. Another nurse called the Resident and a Respiratory Therapist to the bedside. No one could believe what they were seeing. This patient, who had been comatose for almost a week, suddenly woke up on Christmas morning.

His mother, who usually called very early in the

morning to inquire how his night was, checked in on him, as usual. I was thrilled she called before the end of my shift, because I was able to give her the news that he woke up, and that neurologically, he seemed "normal." She wanted to see him; she lived not far from the hospital, and told us she could be there in about twenty minutes. Perfect. That gave us enough time to perform a couple quick tests, and we were able to extubate him and replace the breathing tube with a simple oxygen facemask. When she walked toward the bed, she heard his voice and started crying. There were probably times last week when she wondered whether she was ever going to hear him speak again.

"Merry Christmas, John. It's Christmas morning."

I don't know if it's because John's mother was crying, or because of the beautiful traditional Christmas music playing on the TV, but I started to cry as well.

I was standing next to my coworkers, and I said to no one in particular, "It's a Christmas Miracle."

The others nodded, and our hearts were touched by watching the relieved mother sitting on the edge of John's bed, hugging and kissing her son. We were all moved to tears; there wasn't a dry eye among any of the staff in the ICU. What better gift could a mother receive on Christmas than knowing her son was alive and well?

Over twenty-five years later, I still clearly remember that Christmas morning. I hope I never forget it.

Am I Dreaming?

Our ICU night shift crew worked well together. Whether we were receiving a new admission from the ER or accepting a fresh surgical patient from the OR, we worked as a team. We worked efficiently, each of us fulfilling a certain duty. Some of us enjoyed phlebotomy, others untangled IV lines, some managed the medications, while others documented information in the chart. We divided up the duties, somehow knowing who preferred a particular task.

It was no different when it came to cardiac arrests, commonly known as "code blue." We rarely called a code over the loudspeaker system. Instead, we managed the emergency ourselves. Making an announcement brought too many extraneous people to the scene, then crowd control became a problem. If a particular doctor or physician assistant wasn't present, we knew how to reach them via direct phone extension or beeper system. Additionally, all the ICU nurses were Advanced Cardiac Life Support (ACLS) certified, which was a requirement for the job. This certification involved taking a class, passing a written test, and demonstrating skills needed to run a code blue. To ensure we maintained ACLS proficiency, we needed to renew this certification every two years. ICU nurses knew what to do at the beginning of a Code, and managed the patient until further help arrived, if needed.

Our eyes and ears were always alert for what we called the "triple star" alarms, meaning someone was in a lethal cardiac rhythm or had an abnormally low blood pressure. Immediate response was always the best initial course of action. "Time is muscle" is a phrase that we were taught. Whether talking about someone having a myocardial infarction or a cardiac arrest, the sooner appropriate intervention was received, the better. Lack of blood circulation leads to lack of perfusion to major body organs, such as the brain, heart, or kidneys. When heart muscle dies, that dead part doesn't come back to life, affecting future function.

When we heard a three-star alarm one night, we all turned to look at the central monitor, and saw that a patient was in a lethal ventricular tachycardia rhythm, also known simply as "V-tach." We stopped what we were doing and sprang into action. Two nurses ran toward the patient's room; another two grabbed the defibrillator and "code cart." Someone else was calling the doctor and the Respiratory Therapist.

After checking for a carotid pulse and finding none,

one of the nurses began CPR. This experienced nurse didn't hesitate starting cardiac compressions, and knew that high quality compressions were the most effective ones. While leaning over the patient, she was audibly counting out loud the number of times his chest went up and down. She was a rather large-breasted woman, so her breasts were also keeping time, bouncing around with the beat of each compression.

Fortunately, this was an extremely quick code, consisting of less than a minute of compressions. We hadn't even had time to administer any medications or attach the defibrillator pads when the patient almost immediately woke up. When he looked forward, all he could see were my colleague's enormous boobs in his face. She stopped the CPR for a few moments, but remained leaning over his body, ready to resume compressions in case he became unconscious again.

"Am I dreaming?" was all the patient could say.

"Yeah, he's okay," we said to each other.

We laughed, knowing that seeing a woman's deep cleavage hanging in front of him probably was what that old man dreamed about. We told the nurse she better back away from the bed, because he might go into cardiac arrest again for a completely different reason. No, Mr. Davis, you weren't dreaming.

Old Buzzard

Working at night could be full of harmless, pre-planned fun at times. Occasionally, someone would come up with an idea for a "theme night" in which we would each bring in food of a specific nature. Sometimes we'd have all the ingredients to create a huge ice cream sundae buffet, or we'd obtain Mexican food and celebrate Cinco de Mayo. On holidays or during the various seasons, nurses wore colorful printed scrubs or funny jewelry.

The "Old Buzzard" in this particular chapter was the reason for one particularly festive night. No, the old buzzard wasn't an elderly patient; it was ME. You see, my birthday was coming up soon, and I was going to be a whopping thirty years old. In good, clean fun, the night crew planned to celebrate in advance my birthday at work. They had conspired to make it a special and memorable event and were very successful at keeping it a secret from me.

30th Birthday cake

On the night of the planned party, one of the nurses asked me to help her bathe and reposition her patient, who was located in the furthest corner of the ICU. She lured me to her patient's bedside and closed the curtains. Nothing she did was suspicious, because we routinely ensured the patient had privacy while we helped each other provide care. She wasn't rushing through anything she was doing and engaged me in conversation. Not being needed in her patient's room any longer, I rewashed my hands and proceeded back to the central charting area and break room.

The lights had been dimmed. As I entered the break room and turned on the lights, my colleagues yelled, "SURPRISE!" followed by singing a somewhat harmonious rendition of "Happy Birthday." A beautiful cake, which was decorated on top to resemble the face of my English Bulldog puppy, sat in the center of the table. Streamers of black ribbon and black balloons graced the walls. There were also snacks—both healthy and fattening varieties—available for munching. Naturally, we started with cake first, and we all had our nighttime break together. I was shocked and touched by their kindness and humor.

The fun continued that night, as I began finding stickers attached to walls and equipment in various places in the ICU. The corner of a monitor, the bathroom mirror, and a doorframe were just a few of the places where I found the birthday stickers. The images were of old buzzards and tombstones, or stated things such as "old fart" or "over the hill." It was like a fun little treasure hunt game, seeing how many of those stickers I could find during the night. They appeared where I least expected. What was even more ironic and funny is that I knew I was the youngest employee working in the ICU on the night shift. At the age of thirty, I actually think I was the youngest employee on any shift in the ICU at that time.

Thank you, everyone, for that awesome pre-birthday night. Many of you probably don't remember doing that for me, but I do. In many different ways, I certainly worked with a fantastic group of nurses and respiratory therapists.

Barnyard Noises

The strangest things sometimes happen at night. Nurses are fond of blaming unusual events on a full moon. Although I know there are some people who aren't convinced that a patient's behavior and the phase of the moon are related, I agree with the majority of nurses who believe some of the craziest events happen during this time of the lunar cycle. More than a few times in my career, I've heard a nurse who was having a terrible shift ask, "Is it a full moon tonight?"

Another superstition many nurses embrace involves the use of the "Q" word. In the case of nursing, "Q" stands for the word "quiet." Don't dare say to anyone as you're leaving to go home, "See you later, I hope you have a quiet night." Usually, a collective groan is made by the nurses who are starting their shift because they know a horrible night is probably in store for them.

Sometimes we're quick enough to hush someone and say, "Shhhhhhh!" when another nurse starts to say, "It was a really great day, you'll probably have a qu…"

Personally, my least favorite phrase originated from an evening nurse who routinely gave me my shift report. Often, she happily knocked her knuckles on an ICU table and said, "The patient is *rock stable.*" She was a very competent nurse, and I wanted to believe her. But usually upon entering the patient's room, I'd find some kind of disaster. The patient may have ripped out an IV which was infusing crucial medication, or they were hypotensive, or bleeding all over everything. Perhaps the patient started projectile vomiting or had a sudden onset of massive diarrhea. Regardless of what catastrophe happened at the start of my shift with her former patients, I'd spring into action while shaking my head in disbelief.

On a different night which began easily enough, my patient became very verbal as midnight approached, but he wasn't yelling anything that anyone could understand. He wasn't speaking in a foreign language or talking in incoherent speech, which sometimes we called "word salad." It didn't look like he was having a cardiovascular accident, also known as a "stroke," either. What was he doing? He was making barnyard noises, which sounded like a combination of a cow mooing while having a calf and a donkey being strangled. They were hideous, loud noises. I couldn't reason with or soothe this confused individual; he needed medication. The sounds emitting from his mouth were continuous and the other nurses were telling me I had to do something about this situation. They didn't want their own patients disturbed or woken up by his utterances.

Fortunately, I was working with one of my favorite cardiac physician assistants (PA-C) that night, and he was responsible for overseeing this patient's care. I called him on the phone and described the situation. However, since the patient was rather elderly, he didn't want to prescribe any sedative medication.

"The yelling is good for his lungs because he's taking deep breaths," I was told. The other nurses were dismayed that I couldn't quiet down the patient and he continued his mooing and braying.

After more time went by, my fellow nurses urged me, "Ann, you've got to do something about it. Call the PA again."

I called the PA-C once more and tried to do a better job of explaining the situation. He was notified that the patient wasn't exactly yelling, but making some very strange animal noises. I received an order for a miniscule amount of sedative. The medication took a while before it calmed the patient slightly, and the effects were short lived.

The other nurses were continuing to complain, but then one of them said, "I have an idea." She retrieved a portable phone and plugged it into the outlet near my patient's bed. "Call him again" she urged.

I think I understood her idea. After dialing the number to the PA-C's on-call room, I was a little hesitant to speak when he answered the phone. It was now about two o'clock in the morning, and I knew he wanted to get some sleep.

"Uh, hi. Yeah, it's me again. I have someone who wants to talk to you."

Then I held the phone near the patient's mouth as he made those gruesome, peace-shattering sounds. After letting the PA listen to it for about thirty seconds, I brought the phone receiver back to my own face.

"Did you understand all that?" I asked. "He was begging for something to help him sleep a little bit tonight."

Fortunately, the PA-C who was on duty had a fantastic sense of humor, and I rarely saw him get angry. He gave me an order for an additional small dose of sedative. That extra portion helped silence the patient and allowed him to rest noiselessly through the remainder of the night. Unbelievably, a calm atmosphere was restored in the ICU. The barnyard animals were no longer heard.

Hide Me

Probably one of the most satisfying things about being a nurse is knowing you helped someone get well, and then seeing that they were able to successfully get discharged from the hospital and go home. One of the primary goals of our job is making people better, isn't it? After our patients left the ICU, we usually never knew what happened to them. If one of them died before leaving the hospital, though, we usually heard about that. When a patient sent us a kind note, thanking us for the care we provided, we learned they were doing well. Once in a great while, a patient actually voluntarily came back to the hospital and personally thanked us.

Therefore, I was initially thrilled to see one of my former patients at a local gym where I had a membership. I wasn't sure it was actually him at first, but he had definitely recognized me. It's different seeing someone wearing "normal" clothes and walking around versus laying in a bed wearing a hospital gown. He looked healthy, and told me he had joined the gym in order to build his strength after being sick for a long time. I had routinely taken care of him for perhaps a couple months. After telling him I was happy that he successfully made it out of the hospital and was doing well, I said goodbye and continued with my exercise workout.

There was a time in my life when I frequently went to the gym. While enjoying the circuit training machines, I could efficiently get a lot accomplished, keep my weight under control, and build muscle. That was before I realized how much more I preferred to exercise outdoors, by riding a bicycle, walking, or hiking. I'm happiest when I'm outside in fresh air, regardless of my choice of activity. But back then, I made the effort to visit the gym several times a week.

The next time I visited the gym, my former patient was also there. He stopped to chat with me again. He was friendly and I didn't see any harm in talking with him once in a while. The problem, however, is that the scenario kept replaying each time I went to the gym. I'd walk in the door of the facility, and not long after that, he'd spot me and come over to talk with me. Saying "hello" was fine, but he kept reliving his hospitalization experience, describing it in great detail. The conversation was basically always the same, with him speaking about his illness. I was noticing how much time I spent with him, time which was time stolen from my exercise routine. The long interactions with him had to stop.

When I walked through the doorway of the gym, we waved hello to each other, but I didn't walk toward him or initiate any conversation. In an effort to avoid him, I immediately started my workout, but he'd follow me wherever I went. If I was on a treadmill, he'd choose a machine next to mine, and restart his narration about his illness. Literally, the only place where I could go to escape was the women's locker room.

I know it was not his intention to ask me to be his girlfriend, because the majority of time I arrived at the gym with my future husband, Wayne. Since I introduced him to Wayne, the former patient knew I was already in a committed relationship. If he was lonely, there were multiple other people with whom he could speak at the gym. Nurses are perceived to be caring or sympathetic individuals, which may be why he wanted to speak with me whenever possible. But we are people first, nurses second. It's doubtful that anyone wants to be considered "on duty" twenty-four hours a day, especially on a day off from work. I can only speak for myself, of course, when I say I like to keep my home and work life distinctly separate.

Unwilling to be rude to the former patient who I now saw at the gym every time I arrived there, I simply wanted to hide. But there was nowhere to hide while using any of the equipment. When it was time for my gym membership to be renewed, I let it expire. Since I was no longer enjoying going to the gym, I found other ways to exercise. Perhaps this gentleman did me a favor. I started riding my bicycle more and going to the local state park. I tried jogging, although I'm extremely slow and don't enjoy it as much as other activities.

My future husband soon understood why I didn't want to return to the gym. Having seen us together and been introduced, my former patient now sought out and spoke a lot to Wayne. Since I wasn't available to listen to him any longer, he now haunted my fiancé. Wayne isn't a nurse and didn't care about the other guy's self-centered issues or medical problems. He didn't want to explain to him why I wasn't going to the gym any longer, or tell him anything about me, either.

"You're right, there's nowhere to hide from him," he acknowledged.

I laughed, saying, "At least I could go to the female locker room, but you can't even escape him at the toilet."

Soon after that, Wayne stopped going to the gym, as well. We both utilized the public park and rode our bicycles together. I continue to exercise outside, now mostly by myself.

First Admission

One of the first things most nurses do when they start their shift is look at the patient assignment sheet. It gives you the name and room number of who you'll be caring for while you're at work. On our worksheet, which was always posted at the nurses' station, it also listed the name of the nurse in charge. Happily, I might sometimes see "#1 OH" listed under my name, which meant I was taking care of the first surgical cardiac case of the day. That was almost always my favorite type of assignment. I tried not to let out a groan whenever I saw "1st Admit" listed underneath my name.

"First Admit" meant you might have a really great night, or a terrible one. It was a roll of the dice. Sometimes you were lucky, and other times you were not. What those words essentially meant was that you started your shift with one relatively easy patient. Then, whoever was the next patient who rolled into the ICU was going to be your second customer. Sometimes the charge nurse already knew in advance that there was someone in the ER or on one of the upstairs wards who needed to be treated in the ICU. Therefore, she could give you a quick synopsis of what to expect. Often, no one needed ICU care urgently, so you just waited to see who might be sent your way. An ambulance might bring someone to the hospital in the middle of the night, or there might be someone in respiratory distress, or a code blue which necessitated ICU care. On rare occasions, you didn't get any admission at all.

On one August night, I had made it to four in the morning without hearing about any patient needing to come my way. I was almost ready to do a little victory dance, but that moment of glee was short lived. Over the loudspeaker system, I heard the Operator say, "Code blue, X-ray. Code blue, X-ray." Just before the end of my shift, the patient would probably be under my care. But with codes, you never knew if they'd survive long enough to make it to the ICU; sometimes the patient couldn't be revived.

Hearing the announcement made all of us working that night try to complete our lab drawing duties, vital signs, etc. in a timely basis. If the coding patient made it to the ICU, we'd all soon be very busy, even though they would primarily be my patient. We worked as a team because it was almost impossible to admit a new patient completely by yourself, especially someone as sick as a person who coded.

Rita Watt

As I walked toward the empty room where my future patient would be received, the nurse in charge approached me with a piece of paper in her hand.

Out of the blue, she asked me, "What's your mother-in-law's name?" *Huh?* She repeated, a little more emphatically this time, "What's your mother-in-law's name?"

She was asking because my mother-in-law was actually not my official relative yet, although I considered her family. Wayne and I had been together for ten years, and we were finally going to get married in autumn. We lived together, and my future in-laws' house was directly behind ours, in a suburb of Providence. Since the ceremony hadn't occurred yet, I was still using my long, Polish, maiden name.

"Rita," I finally replied. "Her name is Rita Watt."

The charge nurse handed me the piece of paper which was in her hand. It was an arterial blood gas slip, an "ABG." The first thing I saw at the top was my mother-in-law's name, followed by the test results. The Ph was 6.9, an extremely poor figure, not compatible with life. I let out a gasp. My admission was going to be my future husband's mother.

I yelled to the charge nurse, "Watch my patient!" as I ran out the door as fast as I could toward the ER.

Unbeknownst to me, my mother-in-law had been brought to the ER earlier in the night because she wasn't feeling well. No one had notified me, otherwise I probably would have made the effort to check on her and say hello during my dinner break.

She had a variety of medical issues and had been slowly declining over the past few years. She was still living at home with my father-in-law, but it was starting to look like she may need nursing home care in the near future. No one wanted to discuss that option because she was neurologically intact and would definitely reject that idea. Taking care of an elderly parent is often extremely difficult—physically and mentally—on both the parent and the caregivers. Difficult decisions often need to be made; it's almost impossible finding a compromise which keeps everyone happy.

When I arrived in the ER, I quickly found the room where she was located. The code was over, but she was alive, intubated, and ventilated, with a peaceful look on her face. When I scanned her cardiac monitor, I saw she had an adequate blood pressure and heart rate, probably significantly better than mine was at the moment. The ER nurse looked shocked to see me, and I had to explain who I was in relation to her patient. Even though I had rushed to the ER, I was too late to stop the code in progress. Rita had previously expressed that she wanted to have a DNR status, and had documentation to prove it at home. I knew that I didn't actually have the authority to stop the code, but I could have called my future husband, and he would have intervened on her behalf. His dad had gone home because it was late at night and he had been waiting with her in the ER for a long time. It originally looked like a routine admission for her, nothing to be too worried about.

What happened? She was generally feeling lousy all day before she finally agreed to go to the hospital. It seemed like she might have had pneumonia. She had been placed in a wheelchair and was taken for a chest X-ray. While she was in the radiology department, which was next to—but not actually in—the ER, she collapsed. The only person with her was the X-ray Tech; no other nurses or doctors were present. The code was called, and because of her location and circumstances, she probably went without oxygen for a significant amount of time. The result was that she ended up respiratory arresting, which progressed to a cardiac arrest. Hypoxic too long, she developed an anoxic brain injury. Yes, she was brain dead, which was later confirmed through additional testing.

I never admitted her as my patient; I was told to

immediately go home instead. Wayne was surprised when I arrived home early, and he was stunned as I began to tell him the news about what happened to his mother. Other family members were notified a few hours later. Several of us attended a family care conference the next day, which was led by my ICU Director. He explained to our family what had happened, and the implications and options for her future were also discussed. Even though I had tried to explain all these things to our family, it needed to be heard from a doctor who was a neutral party. I respected the current ICU Director and knew he would do an excellent job relaying this information in a sensitive manner. The decision was made to make her "comfort measures only" (CMO) status and remove her from the ventilator. I knew she would imminently die if she did not receive breathing assistance. One by one, relatives who were present briefly said goodbye and left. No one except Wayne and me stayed at her bedside while she was actually dying. Her heart quickly stopped.

Eventually, all nurses experience what it's like seeing their own family member, close friend, or colleague as a patient in a hospital. I wish I could say that the medical education and experiences we possess make those times easier for us. Occasionally, having medical knowledge causes us anxiety or great sadness because we understand the harsh reality of what is happening to our loved one. We can't hide behind ignorance, and we can't flick a switch and turn off what we've learned or witnessed in the past.

Knowledge is usually power, but often, we are left just as helpless as anyone else to cure those about whom we care. Illness and disease are real, and they can be cruel. Unfortunately, despite our best efforts, we can't save everyone all the time, including people who are dear to us.

Free Advice

If you happen to be a nursing student or fairly new RN, I'll give you a little free advice: don't give out free advice. Obviously, I'm talking about medical advice. Most seasoned nurses already know this.

I've always been proud to be a nurse, although I learned not to advertise that fact. Through various things you may say to another person during a conversation, many people can guess you are a nurse or in the medical profession. If you're a woman, you're probably going to find that most people will ask, "Are you a nurse?" Why don't they ask if you're a surgeon, anesthesiologist, cardiologist, or a pharmacist? I can be standing beside a male colleague, and someone often assumes he is the doctor, and I am the nurse. I've often wanted to reply, "Actually, no. I'm a neurosurgeon." Knowing my luck, the person with whom I'd be speaking would probably respond, "Wow, imagine that. I'm a neurosurgeon, too.

Tell me, what was the biggest meningioma you ever resected?" Then I'd have to confess I lied.

Unfortunately, sexism still exists. It was never my intent to fill this book with a bunch of statistics, so I don't know how many men are currently nurses and how many women are doctors.

Once you become a nurse, it's sometimes difficult to adjust the language you use when conversing with someone else. If I'm speaking with a patient or family member, I'll attempt to say "stroke" instead of "CVA," or "you have high blood pressure" rather than "hypertension." I'm not talking to someone as if they're ignorant; I merely want them to understand what I'm saying. Someone is always free to interrupt and tell me they work in a medical field, at which point I'll start using appropriate medical terms. I'm not assuming that only people in the medical profession are reading my stories. In case you haven't noticed by now, there is a brief glossary of medical terms and abbreviations in the back of this book.

Another clue that catches someone's attention is if you happen to mention that you work night shift. I suppose someone could guess that I may work in a factory or warehouse when I say that, but usually the first thought that comes to mind is the nursing profession.

When I travel, mostly for vacation, I prefer not to talk about anything related to medicine or work. Vacations are my free time to think about things I enjoy, not a time to be quizzed about my job. Many individuals are simply trying to be friendly and pass the time on an airplane when they inquire, "What do you do for a living?" I'd usually answer honestly and tell the person I'm a nurse. About 50 percent of the time, I'd regret that answer. Not because I'm embarrassed that I'm a nurse, or have anything to hide. I only regret my reply when the conversation continues in a direction that I dislike, such as when a person wants sympathy and proceeds to tell you about every ache and pain they've ever had in their life.

One time a fellow vacationer told me that he was an infectious disease specialist. He kept steering the conversation in order to talk about HIV and AIDS, constantly throwing statistics at me and talking about CD4 counts, etc., etc. He kept talking because he thought he was so smart—which he probably was—and enjoyed hearing himself speak. I could not have cared less, and had no desire to spend my precious vacation time being educated about his specialty. From that point on, I started daydreaming about telling people I had a dog walking business, or was a salesperson at the jewelry counter in a department store—any career that would allow me to bluff my way through a conversation. Yes, I know. If someone else is determined to talk about themselves, they will do so, regardless of what I say.

Other people seize the opportunity to obtain free medical advice when they learn you're a nurse, which is actually the main point of this chapter. Why would they ask for medical advice from a stranger? Maybe they don't have a primary physician, or don't like their doctor. Perhaps they're trying to save money on copayments or don't want to make an actual appointment. It could be a multitude of personal reasons. They have no idea that's it's not fair to you, or that it could be dangerous, solicitating such advice. You won't have their entire medical history or lab results in front of you. How are you expected to make a diagnosis when given general information without specifics? If you give someone incorrect or inappropriate information, there is always the possibility that that person may attempt to sue you for malpractice. This is especially true if you tell someone you don't think their condition is very serious and it turns out to be severe or fatal. If a person does not seek appropriate and prompt care because you felt it was unnecessary, and they are harmed by your bad advice, you've created a whole lot of trouble for yourself.

So, what should a nurse do when someone who is not their patient seeks medical advice from them outside of their work environment? Some nurses are amazing, and have the ability to bluntly say, "I don't give out free medical advice. *Ever.*" And they leave it at that. That tactic never seemed to work for me, since the individual would keep pressing me for answers. If you're in a confined environment such as an airline seat, it's extremely difficult to simply excuse yourself, get up, and walk away.

I utilize a different tactic, one which I think shows concern, but at the same time, saves me from jeopardizing my nursing license. With a tone of concern, I'd say to an advice seeker, "Oooooooh, that sounds like it could be serious. You really need to go to a doctor about that sooner rather than later, or seek care in an emergency room." Regardless of what I said, I always, always, *always* advised someone to go see a doctor.

What I always found humorous was when someone would start saying to me, "I have a *friend* who has a medical problem...." Ah, the infamous "friend" line. Then they would continue with saying something such as, "He has a wart or some kind of growth on his butt," or, "He's having some sexual dysfunction." Wow, I'm impressed that you have such a close friend who is willing to divulge those kinds of details to you. But what's funnier is the fact that, because I'm a nurse, I'm expected to be an expert in every avenue of nursing. No, I don't know why your kid is puking. I've never had a baby, and I don't know how much weight you can safely gain during pregnancy or how long it's going to take to lose your acquired pregnancy weight. I'm not a urologist or a proctologist, and I definitely don't know anything about cancer or chemotherapy. Sure, we are taught a variety of things in nursing school and need to pass a written exam before we officially become registered nurses, but after that, a lot of us go into specialty areas. Personally, my mind is not a sponge, absorbing every medical detail in every specialty. I focused on adult care critical care. I'm not going speculate on pediatric or oncology issues.

One last word on the topic of advice. It's been my experience that most families are thrilled when one of their relatives goes into the medical profession. What parent isn't proud when he or she states, "My daughter is a doctor," or, "My daughter became a nurse"? But that's usually where the excitement stops. After you've earned your license, try telling your father, "You really need to stop smoking, you'll get lung cancer. I've taken care of a lot of people who needed a lung removed because they were lifelong smokers." It doesn't matter how much you tell a parent or spouse, "I love you, but you really shouldn't eat all that fatty stuff, you'll get heart disease. I don't want to see you in the hospital having cardiac bypass surgery." Try advising someone they really need to take their medication properly and not adjust the dosages any way they want. Everyone wants to have a nurse in the family, but when it comes to their own care, your expertise may not be valued, and you may be informed to mind your own business. With family, you can try to give helpful advice if you dare. But it probably won't be heeded. Such is the life of a nurse.

Please Don't Honk the Horn

Working the night shift isn't always easy, for a variety of reasons. But for many nurses, it's an active choice we've made. Many night nurses have children, so they've chosen to split a 24-hour day with their spouse. The husband, working day shift, spends time at night with the children, hopefully assisting with homework and tucking them in to bed. The mother, at home during the day, ensures the children get off the bus safely and have something to eat for dinner. If a child is sick, or school is cancelled because of weather, at least one of the parents is available to watch the child. Unfortunately, that often means that the night nurse foregoes getting any sleep when a child needs to be watched. I've worked with many sleep-deprived nurses over the years, but they work nights because they love their children, and it usually works out for the best for their family.

Some nurses work night shift because of the nightly shift differential they earn. Unbelievably, this shift differential used to be close to what the minimum wage was in the United States. By working at night, you could be earning what was the equivalent of someone actually working two different jobs in a non-medical field. Of course, this amount could be higher or lower, depending on whether you worked in a large metro area or a more rural setting. I definitely enjoyed the added pay, and truly appreciated it. If I worked day shift, I'd have to work more hours to achieve an equivalent pay to what I earned at night.

Many nurses, including myself, enjoyed the autonomy we were able to use on the night shift. We didn't have anyone looking over our shoulders every second of the day. We were responsible, organized, and made decisions appropriately. Much thought was put into phone calls made to physicians or physician assistants before we actually dialed their number. We tried to make one phone call to an MD instead of three different successive calls within a few minutes.

Of course, upper management wasn't walking through the unit at night; they worked different hours. When the Joint Commission on Accreditation of Healthcare Organizations (JCAHO) arrived at the hospital to perform inspections, it was always during the day shift. I don't know if that has changed in recent years, but night nurses were thrilled that we were departing our facility just as JCAHO personnel were arriving.

And finally, most family members visit during the day, or into the early part of the evening. The hospital in which I worked had instituted "open visiting hours" for families of patients in the critical care areas. It actually was a good policy because it allowed families to visit at any time of the day in ICU; they were not limited to specific hours. Of course, limitations were placed on visits at times, such as when we were performing a procedure on the patient. The visitor had to wait until the procedure was over. Being a night shift nurse, I know how I would have felt if I wasn't allowed to visit a family member because I couldn't arrive at a specific time. My sleep and wake cycles would have made it difficult to visit. For example, I appreciated being able to leave work and quickly visit my ill Father-in-Law before I headed home. Driving from home on my day off to go see him usually took up more time than the actual visit itself. Seeing him immediately after my shift while in the Providence area was an efficient use of my time. But for the most part, the majority of visitors arrive at the hospital during the daytime.

Other nurses were somewhat forced into working the night shift; it wasn't their choice. That was me, in the beginning of my career. The only jobs available were night jobs because day shift was in such high demand. But I ended up loving working 12-hour night shifts, and I was mostly employed in that type of position for the majority of my career.

It wasn't the night shift itself that I didn't like at times; it was the inability to sleep. Ordinarily, I had no problems sleeping. I was able to shut thoughts out of my mind and fell asleep easily. I didn't have children, so my house itself was relatively quiet. Wayne knew not to make excessive noise, because he'd pay the price if he woke me up before I was ready to crawl out of bed. Unfortunately, I couldn't control noise made by my neighbors or the children who lived in the vicinity.

My next-door neighbor was a friendly woman. One year she decided she'd earn a little extra cash through babysitting or running a home daycare. I'm sure she took excellent care of the children she was watching each weekday. They were quiet, probably engrossed in reading books or involved in some other activity. My problem with her new endeavor was when a certain parent arrived to pick up her child in the afternoon. Afternoon was the middle of my sleep time. Think of it this way: Two o'clock in the morning for most people who worked a nine-to-five job was equivalent to me being asleep at two o'clock in the afternoon. You're in bed and have to wake up in a few hours. You don't want to be woken any sooner, because you might not be able to fall back asleep if you do. Lack of sleep often equated with having a lousy or unproductive day at work. I knew that most people didn't comprehend the crazy work-sleep cycles in my life; it was not what most people considered "normal." My life was lived opposite of how the world generally functioned.

The parent, probably unaware that a night shift nurse

lived next to her child's caregiver, *always* tooted the car horn when she was pulling out of the driveway. At first, I hoped that it was only going to be a once-in-a-while honking, but those hopes were crushed. That parent honked the horn every stinking time she picked up the kid at my neighbor's house. It was getting aggravating, because it always woke me up, often out of a sound sleep. Then, I began having problems sleeping at times, out of anticipation of the honking horn. I don't do well when I don't get adequate sleep. I've often told people who know me, "If I don't eat food, I'll survive, but if you rob me of sleep, I turn into a monster!" You really don't want to be around me when I'm sleep deprived.

Finally, I decided I had to say something to my neighbor about the parent's horn beeping. I thought very carefully about how I would bring up the subject and what I wanted to say. Not wanting to create any animosity between us by a poor choice of words, I was determined to plead my case in a diplomatic manner. I calmly strolled over to her house on my next day off. She was somewhat surprised to see me at her front door.

"Do you have a few free minutes?" I politely asked. She stated she had time for a conversation, so I continued. "I wanted to talk to you about the parent who arrives to pick up her child each weekday afternoon." She stood quietly while I continued. "Since I've lived next to you for several years, I'm sure you know I work night shift." She nodded. "I sleep during the day. When that parent beeps the horn as she's leaving your driveway, it wakes me up every single time she does it.

Could you please ask her to only wave goodbye and not honk the car horn anymore?"

Her reply totally dumbfounded me. She said, with a shocked look on her face, "Why, I couldn't possibly do that."

I was almost speechless, but I asked her, "Why not?"

She acted as if my request was completely ridiculous, irrational, or extreme. Once again, she told me, "I can't possibly do that."

She wasn't going to comply. She was more concerned about what the parent thought and didn't care whatsoever about her next-door neighbor. I truly did not think I was making an unreasonable request. I'm a *nurse*. I need to be able to get some sleep in order to function well. Would you want a sleep-deprived person taking care of your family member? I wasn't asking her to give up her daycare or do anything particularly special for me. I could not understand why she wouldn't help me out with this situation. If the roles were reversed, I would have profusely apologized and said something such as, "I had no idea the horn was interrupting your sleep, I'll talk to the child's mother the next time I see her. I'm so sorry, I wish you would have told me sooner. It must be difficult trying to sleep during the daytime with so many random interruptions." You get the idea. I lost a lot of respect for my neighbor that day. I walked away without saying anything else to her. Of course, the horn tooting continued. In retrospect, perhaps I should have spoken directly to the parent about it. Who knows if the response or results would have been different.

Not long after that, Wayne and I purchased land in the countryside and had a house built for us. It involved a longer commute to work, but I didn't mind. The area is much quieter than where I previously lived, although no place is perfect. ATV riders occasionally zoomed up and down the road on the weekends. A night I was working always seemed to coincide with trash day. At least I didn't have to see that neighbor any longer, because I don't know if I'd ever end up saying what was truly on my mind, which was probably something I might regret.

I worked night shift for a total of thirty-two years. Nowadays, I sleep a little later in the morning, and very well at night. Catching up on all that missed sleep, I guess…

Sixteen Beds

After having worked in a combined cardiothoracic and medical/surgical ICU for many years, changes were headed our way. New ICUs were going to be built because our current ICU was too small and we couldn't keep up with demand for our beds. The cardiothoracic and vascular surgeons thought their customers should take precedence over other patients, and they pre-booked beds for their surgical cases. The sick patients who coded or needed a ventilator and critical care expertise couldn't be cared for in any other area, and quickly filled empty beds. Our CCU was too small to accommodate either clientele and they preferred to be exclusive to only cardiac medical patients. Thus, the decision was made to renovate a couple hospital wings on the second floor and create two new units. One was going to be called CVT-S, which was a cardiovascular-thoracic surgical ICU. The other was going to be a general medical-surgical ICU for everything else that needed critical care. A new CCU was also planned at a much later date. The "old" ICU would be permanently closed after the new one was built.

The majority of night nurses seemed to want to gravitate toward the surgical heart unit. First of all, if you took care of one of those surgical patients, you strictly worked with the experienced cardiac physician assistants. You didn't have to deal with the rotating door of Interns and Residents every month. Second, there was a somewhat predictable rhythm on how to care for the cardiothoracic patients. They arrived out of the OR intubated, and usually within a couple of days, they were discharged to the step-down unit. No need to obtain lengthy admission histories—that task was already completed prior to the OR. Overall, the cardiac patients were usually our favorites.

But that was the problem, and management realized it was going to be a big issue. They couldn't allow a mass exodus of experienced nurses from the ICU. If everyone transferred in order to work in the predominantly cardiac unit, no one would be left to staff the new, large, sixteen-bed ICU when it opened. They didn't want it functioning with a completely new staff, so management devised a plan. We were informed that the new surgical heart ICU was only going to employ staff working eight-hour shifts, and required working every other weekend. Currently, except for very few staff members, most of us worked twelve-hour shifts and every third weekend. Everyone was outraged.

Someone such as myself would have to change from working three nights a week to five nights. No one wanted to be committed to being at the hospital more nights, especially if that included working more Fridays and Saturdays. I knew many nurses such as myself who had their calendars marked up almost a year in advance and knew which weekends we were or weren't working. It allowed us to plan vacations and see which holidays we were on duty, or what parties or special events we could attend. The news completely "upset the apple cart," so to speak, for many of us.

We discussed the employment changes among ourselves. Soliciting another person's opinions was okay, but we couldn't allow someone else to make the final decision for us. It was tempting at times to follow the "we'll all stick together" mentality, or toss a coin in the air. Heads it's ICU. Tails it's CVT-S. Ridiculous, right? We would be gambling with our careers and happiness. Those were stressful times.

Day to day, the nurses kept changing their minds on what to do, and indecision was rampant. Making a decision was unavoidable, and we each had to make our individual choice based on what would ultimately be best for ourselves. I ended up picking the ICU because of the twelve-hour shifts. I would be remaining a night nurse, and the amount of nights per week and which weekends I worked were very important to me. I didn't want my schedule changed. Eventually, most of the night staff decided to work in the ICU. After careful consideration, many nurses realized they also prized their schedules and twelve-hour shifts.

Perhaps we also valued each other's companion-ship and the relationships we had built over the years. Commiserating together, we were a unified force and could endure whatever the new ICU brought our way. Our attitudes about the job situation slowly began to change and improve. The night nurses remained a team and started looking forward to working in a modern and spacious, new, sixteen-bed ICU.

Sponge Bath

Trying to take care of personal hygiene as a patient in ICU isn't ideal, as it is at home. Patients, for the most part, weren't allowed to walk to a shower, especially since there probably wasn't one in their hospital room. Occasionally, pre-op patients would be kept in the ICU if there weren't enough available beds on the usual floors. If such patients wanted to shower before their procedure, I'd have to go through the process of meticulously wrapping their IVs so they wouldn't get wet or fall out. I often felt the preparation for the shower actually took longer than the shower itself. What I disliked most was the fact that while a patient was in a shower with the bathroom door closed for privacy, they were unmonitored. One thing I always enjoyed about working in ICU was that the alarms from a cardiac monitor attached to the patient could be heard throughout the unit. Certain waveforms could also be seen from various strategically located monitors in the ICU in addition to the patient's room. You would be instantly notified if any problem was occurring with your patient. Such was not the case if the patient was disconnected from it while in the shower. Later on in my career, pre-op patients were required to bathe with special cloths which were impregnated with a specific antibacterial soap. ICU patients, therefore, were no longer allowed to bathe in the shower at the end of the hall.

Prior to the antibacterial cloths, how were patients bathed? Primarily, a plastic basin was filled with hot water and we used soap and face cloths. The patients who were unconscious or sedated were easily and completely bathed, entirely by nurses. I admit that I don't think anything regarding the human body could surprise me anymore, nor does anything embarrass me. Since I've taken care of patients in all stages of adulthood and who have diverse body shapes, I feel like I've "seen it all." At work, a naked patient was not viewed in a sexual manner. It's just a physical body, and you were doing a job.

I understood that patients may not have felt the same way about the process. Some of the alert patients were embarrassed by needing bathing assistance, but the nurses always tried to calmly reassure them. We kept them covered with towels for privacy, except for the particular body area which we were cleaning. If a patient could do some of the bathing themselves, they were encouraged to do so, and were assisted with the areas of the body they could not reach. Bathing was an ideal time to talk with the patients, and a little bit of education about their care could be incorporated into this activity. An example of this would be demonstrating how to gently pat dry a surgical incision line and informing a patient that the wound should not be roughly rubbed with a towel.

Some of our elderly patients, once in a while, still called these baths "sponge baths." I don't know if actual sponges were ever utilized, but that's the term that was used. My colleague, Martha, had a patient one night who wasn't the least bit embarrassed by being bathed by a nurse. On the contrary, he was looking forward to it.

Martha was one of our more experienced nurses. I don't recall how old she was at the time, and I almost don't dare venturing a guess. Let's say she was somewhere in her middle 50s at the time. Since I'm now in my 50s, I don't consider that age even remotely old, and I try to look good and stay very strong and active. Whatever age Martha was at the time, she looked fantastic and always dressed nicely for the job. I never saw her in scrubs, which was my favorite work attire. Easy to wash and wear, scrubs were definitely my preferred work gear, along with clogs.

I don't recall why Martha's patient was in the ICU, but I can say he was one of the least sick of our current group of patients. He was connected to an IV and the heart monitor, as usual, but otherwise looked well. Most likely, he was going to be transferred to a general medical ward soon, probably that day.

As mentioned earlier in this book, four o'clock in the morning was the usual time for starting duties such as drawing bloodwork, obtaining vital signs, and performing baths. We usually started with the sickest patients first, because they had no idea it was that early in the morning. Sometimes we delayed waking patients until a little bit later because we were sensitive to their need for sleep.

Martha's patient was already awake, so she took advantage of that fact and went to draw his blood. She told him that in a little while she would come back and get him set up so he could bathe. He was an elderly man, perhaps fifteen years or more older than Martha, and he had been leering at Martha whenever he had an opportunity. My own patient's room was next to his, so I witnessed the way he looked at her throughout the course of the night. Not long after the patient's blood was drawn, he was becoming impatient and wanted Martha back in his room. From behind a privacy curtain, I heard him loudly calling, "MAR…THA…I'm ready for my sponge bath!"

To keep him from disturbing any of the other patients with his loud voice, she went into the room to talk to him. I could see the huge grin on his face, and he was lying in bed with his arms and legs spread open, like an oversized gingerbread man. Martha promptly retrieved his bath basin, told him he could get started with washing his face, and explained that she'd be right back.

As she was leaving the room, he was saying to her, "I won't be able to reach and clean everything.

And I feel a little achy, so I'll need a good, long back massage, too."

Trust me, there was nothing wrong with this man's arms or mobility. I'm pretty sure he could reach everything he needed to clean on the front of his body, especially his private parts. His behavior toward Martha was disgusting, but she took it in stride and was more clever than he realized.

"Ann, can you help me out in that room? And where's Mark?" she asked.

I nodded and pointed in the direction of Mark's room across the hall. I followed behind her as she located Mark and asked him if he would please finish up the bath in her own patient's room. "Bribing" him, she told Mark that in return, she'd draw his patients' bloodwork and also administer their medications if he helped her out with her request. Mark thought it was a fair trade, and we walked back to Martha's patient's room. As we were approaching the doorway, we could hear the patient saying, "MAR...THA...I'm waiting!"

Mark and I looked at each other, and I couldn't refrain from giggling. This patient was in for a big surprise. You see, Mark was tall and very muscular with tattoos on his arms. He could be a lot of fun to work with at night, but he could also look stern at times. Most patients didn't give this male nurse any grief, unless they were behaving inappropriately because they were confused.

When we walked into Martha's patient's room, Mark asked with a look of seriousness on his face, "Are you ready for your backrub?"

The look of shock on the man's face was priceless, I wish Martha could have seen it.

He hurriedly asked, "Who are you? Where's Martha?"

Mark answered, "Sir, her other patient had a problem which needed her immediate attention. She asked us to take over so you don't have to wait."

Mark strode toward the bed and directed the patient to turn toward me so he could wash and rub his back. Looking defeated, the patient did as he was told. We helped him finish his bath, changed the bed linens, tidied up the room, and then departed.

Hurrah for Martha. She found a way to put that man in his place, without ever saying an unkind word to him or drawing more attention to his sexist mannerisms. His care was not neglected; it was strategically provided by someone else that morning.

It's Spelled Wrong

I admitted a sweet and calm, elderly woman into the ICU one evening. She was coherent, answered all my questions, and was cooperative with my care. However, she did become a bit distraught after noticing a piece of cardboard posted on the wall which listed her name. The paper was something we placed in the room, which included a patient's name, as well as that of their doctor. It was basically a quick way to identify the patient and under which specialty her care was being directed. Several different surgeons as well as medical doctors utilized our ICU. Proper identification for drawing or administering blood or providing medications actually included looking at and scanning a patient's ID band. In addition, a patient had to verbally state their name and birthdate, if able.

"It's spelled wrong," she stated as she pointed to the paper on the wall.

After looking at her wrist band, I asked her to spell her name. It was correct on her identification bracelet. Next, I looked at my paperwork, and verified that it was also spelled correctly in that location. On the handwritten sign, one of the letters in her name was omitted.

"Yes, you certainly are correct, someone misspelled your name. That's easily fixed; I'll have the secretary make a new sign when I'm finished with a few things in here."

But she wanted it fixed *now*. I assured her that her name was spelled correctly where it mattered the most, on her ID band as well as her paperwork. I promised once again to get the paper on the wall corrected—I first wanted to get her washed and settled for bedtime. She required insertion of a central venous catheter since she had very small veins and no one was able to obtain IV access in her arms. Since she needed multiple IV medications, and probably blood transfusions as well, this special IV catheter would also save her from needless painful phlebotomy attempts. The doctor who had inserted this IV had dripped the antiseptic cleaning solution over various parts of the patient and bed. I wanted to clean everything up and allow the woman to attempt to rest before it got to be late in the evening.

I could relate to my patient's concern over the fact that her name was misspelled. After I fractured my mandible when I was a nursing student, someone from the admissions department came to see me in the ER. She needed some basic information, starting with my name. I pointed to my large student ID tag which was pinned to my uniform. Figuring it would be easier for her to look at and copy my name instead of trying to understand me speaking with a broken jaw, I was dumbfounded when I learned my name was misspelled. She had omitted a letter in my last name, and all of my hospital paperwork was wrong. Why was this a problem? Well, since the name didn't jive with my medical insurance records, the insurance company refused to pay its share of the bills. It was an unbelievable hassle getting the situation remedied, and it wasted a lot of my time and energy. I bet my elderly patient was thinking something like that could happen to her, so she wanted any error immediately fixed.

Even after I enlisted some help from another nurse in order to quickly get her repositioned and clean up the doctor's mess, she continued mentioning her misspelled name. Although I understood her concern, it was beginning to get annoying. I called to the unit secretary via the patient call bell device to request that she make a new name card. She promptly made it for me, and *finally*, the patient stopped talking about it. Continuing to take care of the patient, we started to roll her to the side so we could replace the stained sheets beneath her. Occasionally, when a patient is being turned, the sticky cardiac monitor leads or wires become unattached. Sometimes you didn't realize they're not properly on the patient any longer until the monitor begins beeping. The monitor in this room did alarm, but not in the manner it notified you when it signaled, "leads off."

The heart rhythm showed a flatline, similar to what it looked like when the electrodes were disconnected. After turning the patient back to the supine position, in which she was once again lying on her back, we saw that everything was correctly attached. Other nurses were running toward the room, and we quickly realized that the patient was asystolic. After checking for a pulse and finding none, we immediately began CPR.

The ICU team worked together at length to revive her, but we were unsuccessful. Sometimes, your patient may be talking to you at one moment, then, suddenly or unexpectedly, they will go into cardiac arrest. Even under the best of conditions, such as what she had with two nurses already in her room, sometimes the patient doesn't survive.

After the code was over, the nurse who was originally with me during the bath stayed to clean her up with me the second time. I looked at the dead woman and shook my head in disbelief. Who knows? Maybe my patient knew she was going to die and didn't want her misspelled name on the paper being duplicated in her obituary.

Here Comes
the Bride

Many nurses enjoy a good party or gathering of staff outside of the work environment. It was always fun seeing other nurses dressed in clothes other than their work gear. How different we each could look, when not attired in scrubs or easy-wash-and-wear clothes. Our personalities also often took on a different vibe during a party. We could relax and laugh loudly or tell stories to each other which might not be appropriate for the work environment. Probably the best part of getting together in a casual and fun atmosphere was the fact that if we started a conversation, we could actually finish it. Many times at work, someone may begin to say something and then get interrupted and have to leave the break room, so a story was not completed. Or you may be the one who has to get up and leave, so you never get to hear the end of what was being said. At a party, we were able to talk at length about anything we wanted, for as long as we desired.

After Wayne and I built our new house, I was thinking about hosting a party. Having moved in recently, there wasn't much landscaping done yet, and the interior wasn't fully decorated, either. But I had plenty of space for a small crowd, and I felt ready to entertain guests. I loved where I lived and was happy to invite some people over for a party. For whatever reason, we didn't have an annual gift swap party at someone's house that past December. No one seemed to mind the fact that it was February; we could have a belated Christmas party, anyhow. It might actually be fun exchanging gifts which weren't entirely holiday themed, since spring was approaching.

After reading a unique party theme article in a magazine, I talked to a few people who were going to attend my gathering and presented one of the creative ideas to them. Our colleague, Dawn, was going to be married later in the year. How about having a bridal shower party for her under the guise of it actually being a Christmas party? Better yet, it could be an "ugly bridesmaid dress" party. The magazine article suggested resurrecting old bridesmaid dresses and wearing them during a bridal shower. It sounded like a lot of fun, and we knew Dawn would be completely surprised if we could all keep it a secret.

Plans for the party were made, and everyone attend-

Left: Cindy and Lisa
Right: Dawn with Rey, laughing in the background

ing was going to wear a bridesmaid dress. Some nurses were going to bring extra dresses for those of us who didn't have one any longer. A special cake was ordered, and a bridal veil and bouquet of silk flowers were created for Dawn. I had purchased an audio CD with organ music which contained a traditional version of the bridal march. Guests had purchased gifts for Dawn, and we also had our own swap presents, as well. I was looking forward to the party, and the guest of honor had no clue regarding our hidden agenda.

On the day of the party, it snowed. Yes, I know—snow in New England during the month of February is expected, but we had been enjoying an extremely mild winter that year, with very little accumulation of snow

Left: Jeanne
Right: Patti and Kathy, with Karen in the background

in Rhode Island. I knew everyone with whom I worked was experienced at driving in snow, because we all made it to work on time through that kind of weather. But arriving at work was mandatory, not optional. I was concerned that some people might back out of attending the party because I lived quite a distance from the hospital and you had to traverse some hilly and winding roads to arrive at my home. Everyone who planned on attending, however, showed up as promised. We told Dawn a slightly later party time, allowing us to set up a few things before she arrived.

We kept a watchful eye for her arrival, and she finally approached the house. Scurrying up the stairs to the second floor of my home, the "bridesmaids" lined up for their procession. The door was opened for Dawn, and immediately the veil was crowned on her head and the bouquet of flowers was placed in her hands. I cued the bridal entrance music as our motley-dressed group of friends walked in single file down the stairs toward her. She couldn't have been more shocked, and we had to explain what was going on after we all yelled, "SUR-PRISE!" We told her, "Dawn, it's your bridal shower."

Personally, I had an immense amount of fun at that party. The diversity of dresses we wore was the cause of much laughter. I don't know if it was because of the style of each particular dress, or the fact that most of the dresses didn't fit very well. The gowns were either too long, or too short. There was a colorful assortment of very shiny fabric and scratchy lace. Zippers couldn't be fastened properly, and parts of our bodies bulged in various places. We had gained weight since we originally wore the gown, or the dress we borrowed wasn't made for our body shape. Our shoes, sneakers, and winter boots clashed with the dresses we wore. The dress I was loaned was black velvet with a huge fuchsia pink satin bow on the front. Should I be embarrassed to admit that I rather liked that dress? It was perfect for anyone who was a teenager or young adult during the 80s.

All of the ICU nurses and respiratory therapists, regardless of which shift they worked, were welcome at that party. A party, whether it was that one or a bigger holiday event, fostered cohesiveness among the staff. Like a big family, gatherings outside of work were times when we put aside minor or petty grievances and enjoyed each other's company. Celebrating special life events together created cherished memories for many of us.

Thoughts of that day continue to bring a smile to my face, and I think the attendees also fondly remembered that party for a long time.

An Hour Ago

Working with Interns and Residents could be a pleasure, or a pain in the you-know-what....

I purposely chose to work in a hospital which collaborated with a medical school. Once you get used to having easy access to doctors at any time of the day or night, you might decide against working in a non-teaching facility. There are pros and cons to both, but I decided that a teaching hospital is what I preferred. The added bonus in the hospital where I was employed is that the open-heart surgical program was managed by cardiac surgical Physician Assistants. Unfortunately, at the current time, I was working strictly in the Med/Surg ICU, as previously described.

Most of the doctors with whom I worked with were terrific. As with any job, however, there were some whom I didn't like all that much. Those were the cocky doctors who could be rude or treat the nurses with contempt, as if we were all ignorant. They didn't listen to our suggestions when a patient was having problems, or didn't take our complaints seriously. Sometimes they were too full of themselves to admit when they were wrong, or even to thank the nurses from saving them from making errors. They didn't dare let the ICU Director catch them treating us that way, because he taught them to treat us with respect. The ICU administrator knew that many of us were very experienced nurses, and said that the doctors could learn some things from us. Fortunately, the Interns or Residents who were the "bad" ones were few, and even when there were more than a few, their ICU rotation would be over in a month. We always joked that July was a great month to take vacations, because a brand-new group of Interns would be released from school that month and allowed to bumble their way around the hospital.

There were many doctors who were shining stars, and many who were not. Some of the Residents earnestly wanted to learn something and specialize in critical care, and they were very skilled. Others may have been book-smart, but did the bare minimum. You knew their heart was not into it. Some obviously hated every second of their required ICU rotation. One night, a Resident made it quite clear she did not enjoy her ICU duties.

Sobbing loudly, she lamented, "All I want is to be a Dermatologist. I don't know why they're making me do this month-long torture!"

Similar to nursing students, the doctors needed to show some proficiency in a variety of medical areas, regardless of their intended future specialty. Being a Resident in the ICU was not easy, but most of them suffered in silence and survived. Rarely did we see an embarrassing emotional meltdown as displayed by the future Dermatologist.

Medical students were also part of the parade of medical personnel who had access to the ICU. Similar to the Interns and Residents, a few had much potential, and others didn't. Whether someone was talented or not, I admit I disliked the med students most who would walk into my room with the attitude of, "I'm a future *doctor*—and you're *not*." I mostly avoided those individuals, and only saw them briefly at the end of my shift. They often tried to claim a patient's chart and interrupt while I was in the middle of giving an end-of-shift report to the next nurse caring for my patient. *If you want to get your hands on this chart, you're going to have to get your butt out of bed a lot earlier and grab it.* This was before electronic charting was common, and we relied on paper documentation.

On one particular morning, a medical student entered my patient's room to perform a physical assessment on the patient. I had seen her around the unit on previous mornings and didn't have an opinion about her one way or another. She was a young, Asian woman who was very quiet and appeared a bit shy. That was fine with me—I preferred a meek student over an obnoxious one who might act like he already manages the whole facility. But there is an interesting aspect of this story which you might not expect.

During the course of the night, the family decided to make the patient a DNR. In the midst of a code blue event, his family was called by phone and notified that we were performing CPR and our efforts were becoming futile. The family member mercifully told us to stop "coding" him and allow him to die. The wife and children requested to see him once more and told us they would try to get to the hospital as soon as possible. In the meantime, we cleaned up the patient and his room, removing all evidence of the code. Because of certain circumstances, an autopsy was required on this patient, so we were required to leave all IVs and tubes intact. The ventilator was still attached to him, although it was turned off. He looked like he was calmly sleeping with his eyes closed when the med student entered the room.

Catching up on documentation—because this would be my last opportunity to have access to the patient's chart—I was standing at the end of his bed. When the med student arrived at the bedside, I briefly looked up but said nothing. Expecting the student to leave, I was dumbfounded when she introduced herself to him and started examining the patient. First, she listened to his heart, and then his lungs. She checked a couple other things as well. Did she not notice the IV pumps weren't infusing anything, and that there were no active lights on the ventilator? *Oh yeah, this is going to be good.* Backing away from the bed, I moved to the doorway entrance, standing quietly while observing her actions.

As she was preparing to exit the room, I couldn't resist asking, "Sooooooo, how do you think he's doing today?"

She succinctly replied, "Fine, fine, everything's looking good."

When she reached the doorway, I couldn't make eye contact with her, but I did inform her, "He died an hour ago…"

Her head swiftly turned back to the patient for a few seconds, then she promptly left without saying a word. I never saw her again after that morning.

What's the lesson here? Don't just go through the motions when you examine a patient. Take a long, thorough look, if possible, and do your job well. We're taking care of people, and there's no room for that kind of error.

Mrs. Morretti?

Working in an ICU can be very exciting at times. It's different than the ER, which might be considered "controlled chaos." Some nurses thrive in the unpredictability of either environment. Regardless of how you want to classify life as a nurse in the ICU, it certainly isn't boring. Besides our share of excitement, there was some drama, too. Rumors abounded about nurses dating other staff members. Who dated who never mattered to me, but if the relationship didn't end well, it could quickly become an uncomfortable situation. Once, there was gossip about a couple of people who were caught in a sexual act in the hospital parking lot. Occasionally, there was drama in the ICU waiting room among visitors.

When I was started my shift one evening, my patient's wife, Mrs. Morretti, asked to visit. When she walked into the room, I stated, "Welcome back, it's nice that you're able to visit so often. I'm sure it's comforting to him to hear your voice."

It was a general comment, and she didn't have much to say in return except ask how he was doing today. I thought it was strange that she should ask how he was doing considering she visited him earlier in the day. With certain patients, we often don't see rapid improvements in the course of one day. Maybe she was a little nervous, being in the ICU environment. Sometimes that was simply what people asked when they didn't know what else to say, or they were hungry for good news on a loved one's condition. I gave her an update, then left the room to attend to my other patient's needs. Personally, when I'd take care of a patient for a couple days in a row, improvements in condition weren't always visible. I might know that vital signs or lab values were getting better, but the overall picture of the patient looked the same. Sometimes it wasn't until I came back to work after I'd had a few days off that I saw improvement in a specific patient.

The following night, Mrs. Morretti came back to see her husband again during the evening shift. She asked me the same questions as she did yesterday. She apologized if she was being repetitive with the questions, explaining that it had been a rough day at work for her. She told me it was difficult staying focused on work while her husband was in the hospital. The days seemed very long to her and she wasn't sleeping well at night either. I acknowledged the stress she must be going through at this time, and informed her once again that I'm sure her husband was comforted by hearing her voice. He was intubated and sedated, and could only open his eyes when sedation was minimized to check his neurologic status. Otherwise, he couldn't talk to us—although I always presumed that a patient heard what a person was saying in his room, even toward the end of life. This patient wasn't actively dying, but he needed sedation to allow the ventilator to properly do its job while his lungs healed.

There was more I wanted to say to Mrs. Morretti, but I kept it to myself. I was quite sure the day shift nurse told me that Mrs. Morretti visited every afternoon, and was there that day. The day nurse would be returning to work in the morning, and I wanted to ask her about it.

It was confirmed with the day nurse that there was, indeed, a woman claiming to be Mrs. Morretti who visited every day. She always arrived in the late morning or early afternoon. I told my colleague that a different woman, who visited in the evening, was also claiming to be Mrs. Morretti. There were no family photos posted in the patient's room to identify a spouse. We weren't 100 percent sure which woman was the current, or legal, wife. Perhaps he had two wives. Someone was going to have to figure it out. As for me, my shift was over, and I was off from work for the weekend.

When I returned to work on Monday night, the nurses couldn't wait to tell me some news. "Oh, Ann, you missed it!" they were all saying at once.

"Okay, hurry up and tell me" I said, thirsty for some juicy gossip.

Mr. Morretti's primary day shift nurse was the one who revealed the story. On the weekend, the "real" wife arrived to visit during the day shift, because she didn't work on Saturday or Sunday. She could only visit during the evening on the weekdays because she worked Monday through Friday, approximately nine to five. Someone had called from the waiting room phone, stating she was Mrs. Morretti and wanted to visit her husband. The person who answered the phone stated she'd have to ask the nurse if it was okay, because it looked like the team was working with the patient. She'd send someone to the waiting room to get her when she was allowed to enter. The waiting room was in close proximity to the ICU, so sometimes it was easier walking through the doors to get the visitor.

So, when the visitor was allowed to enter the ICU, a staff member went out to the waiting room and said, "Mrs. Morretti? It's okay for you to come in and visit."

Two women simultaneously stood up. They looked at each other, and tension was in the air. The "real" Mrs. Morretti glared at the other woman, and then briskly strode into the ICU.

No one knew what was later said in that waiting room between the two women. The imposter may have made a hasty departure while possible. Someone had called a security officer to the vicinity of the ICU, "just in case." We were ready for an enormous cat fight between the two of them. Someone later found out, after the patient was extubated and could speak, that one of the women was the patient's wife while the other was his secret girlfriend. Fortunately, I only spoke with the actual legal wife. None of the staff ever saw the girlfriend come back and visit. We don't know if the patient went home and found his wife waiting for him, or if divorce papers greeted him, instead.

I Know What
You're Thinking

Participating in various procedures was part of my job as an ICU nurse. The patients were usually too sick to travel to other departments, so whenever possible, a procedure was performed at the bedside. Examples of this were hemodialysis and endoscopic procedures. Fortunately, those departments brought their own staff with them to oversee and assist, and my involvement was minimal. At other times, such as invasive line insertion, my help was required. I'd obtain equipment, set up the monitor and transducers, hand medications to doctors, etc. I observed sterile technique, documented vital signs, or assisted in any way requested.

When a procedure was being performed by the ICU team, usually a Resident was present, and occasionally an Intern, as well as a Fellow. The Residents were always supervised by a more experienced doctor, such as the Fellow. Sometimes the ICU Director was present, instead.

Because human internal anatomy may vary slightly from person to person, sometimes the procedures took a little longer than usual. Of course, the doctor's skill level also affected how smoothly or quickly a procedure was performed. I'd rather see a procedure performed accurately without causing distress or harm to a patient versus in a speedy manner. However, it was tedious at times observing the extremely slow doctors. Breaking out in a sweat beneath my protective gear, I usually wanted to get off my feet. A hundred other things might also be on my mind, including other duties I needed to complete with both my patients.

One of my favorite Fellows was a doctor we simply called, "Misbah." He had a great personality and was very funny. A terrific team member, he was also appreciated for his skill as a doctor. He explained or demonstrated procedures well to the Residents, guiding their actions with precision. When he conducted a code, it wasn't disorganized or stressful. Instead, he spoke calmly, instructing us on what to do next. Most of us acknowledged that all codes should be directed and performed by emulating his leadership style.

Late one night, I was in a patient's room with Misbah, watching a central line insertion by a Resident. *This is so boring. I have so much to do with this patient when they're done in here. I can't do anything with the patient while the doctors are at the bedside and the sterile drape is in my way. The procedure is dragging on way too long. What is the problem? I really need some coffee right now. What time is it, anyway? If I was Misbah, I would have grabbed the catheter out of the Resident's hand and done it myself by now.* I couldn't leave the area because I was the only non-sterile clothed person circulating in the room. For instance, I might have been needed to retrieve extra supplies from a cart, or manage the heart monitor and keep an eye on vital signs.

After the procedure was completed, Misbah and I were alone in the room with the patient.

He said, "Your face is mostly covered by your mask, but I can tell what's on your mind. The eyes give it all away, I know what you're thinking."

I had to laugh, because I was sure he was correct. He may have been thinking many of the same things. I rarely said much when I was in the room assisting in a procedure because the doctors didn't need any distractions, but Misbah had it all figured out without seeing my entire face or hearing me say anything.

There was one other time I distinctly remember Misbah saying something to me when we were together in a patient's room. I was taking care of an extremely confused patient who was exceptionally obnoxious. He wasn't the least bit cooperative with care, and I had to keep a close eye on him. I was trying so hard to be an empathetic and professional nurse, even though I wanted to yell something very unkind at the patient every time he misbehaved or said something rude to me.

Misbah turned to me and stated, "You have the patience of a saint."

His acknowledgement and compliment meant a lot to me.

The few brief paragraphs about Misbah were included in this book because I found out about fifteen years later that he died. He spent his career saving people and helping them become well, but couldn't save himself when he became ill. He changed his own code status to DNR; it sounded as if he sacrificed his own life in order to spare resources and create an open bed, which someone else utilized. This was during the midst of the COVID-19 crisis. This was what I was told from an outside source, and I believe it was completely true.

What Did He Say?

When vacationing in the Caribbean, I found that most people Wayne and I encountered spoke English exceptionally well. Some sort of accent was usually detected, but we could easily understand what was spoken to us.

As a nurse, I've always tried to enunciate my words well, speaking clearly and sometimes loudly. Many elderly patients don't want to wear their hearing aids and often have difficulty understanding what a nurse is saying to them. Occasionally, they leave the hearing devices at home because they are so costly and they don't want them lost while in the hospital. Fortunately, I have a deeper voice than a lot of women, so it's sometimes easier for a person to hear what I'm saying versus another woman. I always chuckled with the patients, of any gender, who don't mind wearing a hearing aid, saying that sometimes they appreciate not being able to hear well. When their spouse is nagging them about something, they simply "tune them out" by removing the aid. For them, silence is golden.

At the facilities where I worked, doctors and nurses from various regions were employed. Sometimes traveling nurses from the South ended up in the Northeast, and they may have used phraseology which was uncommon to northerners. Occasionally, their accents made it a little difficult to understand them, but this was rare. I worked with doctors from many different countries such as Pakistan, India, or Egypt. Doctors from multiple Asian countries also made their way to Massachusetts or Rhode Island.

To be completely fair, local doctors and nurses were also sometimes difficult to understand. Eastern Massachusetts or Boston accents, or those from Rhode Island, could be challenging at times. I remember when I first moved to Rhode Island, I didn't understand what it meant when I heard a nurse state, "The hot is coming out of the OR in five minutes."

The hot? Ohhhhhh, you mean "the heart."

I grew up in the western side of the state of Massachusetts, and I always pronounce my "R" in a word. Since I've now lived in Rhode Island for thirty years, I'm sure I've picked up a little bit of a different accent. I still giggle when I remember a vacation that I took with Wayne out west. While we conversed with another couple, they exclaimed, "You both sound like the Kennedy family." Ha! I highly doubt that, but it made me laugh and see things from someone else's perspective. Anyhow, I learned to not only speak clearly, but to listen carefully as well.

At the end of the particular trip in the Caribbean, Wayne and I were getting a ride from the hotel to the airport. Standing at the back of the vehicle, Wayne and I heard different things. He heard, "Mumble, mumble, mumble," Then me replying, "Yes, no, okay, no." This was followed by more "mumble, mumble, mumble." I proceeded to get in the vehicle and Wayne followed.

At a later time, Wayne asked, "What did he say?"

"You didn't understand that?" I inquired while laughing.

I translated the muttering for him, telling him that the man had asked, "Are these the only bags you have? Are you in a hurry to get to the airport? I have to pick up a couple more passengers. Do you want me to turn on cold air conditioning for you in the van?"

I guess communicating with medical staff from a variety of regions has its advantages, and patients taught me how to understand mumble. If someone is speaking English, regardless of how badly, broken, or accented, I can understand them.

Hungry

There's one major unspoken rule among staff when you work in a hospital: leave someone else's food alone. If there is something left out on a table, such as in a big bowl or on a platter, it's generally considered fair game. But it's usually pretty obvious if a meal left on a table belongs to one of the staff and has been temporarily abandoned because the employee had to get up to attend to a patient's needs, or an emergency occurred on the unit. I can't say I ever found that to be much of a problem; most people don't want to eat someone else's half-eaten food.

When it came to meals while working at night, I almost always cooked and brought my own food. Plenty of leftovers were usually found in my home after meals because I always made more than enough food. Wayne would have something leftover to eat while I was working and didn't have to think about food preparation after he got home from work. Having pre-packed my lunches, I didn't have to worry about ordering food from any of the local takeout places. Sure, the pizzas and sandwiches which were delivered usually smelled great, and I was occasionally tempted to order, but whenever I did, I never seemed to place an order correctly. I forgot to ask for the dressing I wanted, or specify how much or little I wanted meat cooked, or whether I wanted thick crust or thin. Somehow, I'd have a problem with the takeout food, and was usually disappointed. I'm not truly a picky eater; it should have been simpler than it was. That's how I gave up and decided it was easier to bring my own food. I wouldn't ever be disappointed with my meal, and I saved a lot of money as well.

I could also avoid being elected the person who had to collect the money for a "group order," which was often placed. Ordering as one big group allowed a solitary bag or two of food to be delivered instead of the restaurant person having to make multiple different trips to the hospital. Invariably, sometimes food in an order was accidentally omitted. That was okay if we caught the error and immediately called back to the restaurant. The chef and delivery person usually fixed the problem and brought the food which was left out. However, when we placed an order near the end of closing time, often the restaurant stopped answering their phones before we received the food and realized a mistake was made.

The other thing I didn't enjoy about takeout food was when you didn't get to eat it immediately after it arrived in the unit. Certain foods simply didn't reheat well in a microwave, which was the quickest rewarming option. Often, food wasn't reheated once, but twice. There must have been something about the smell of food which woke up the patients. They could be nicely tucked into bed, but if they weren't intubated and could smell pizza or burgers, they always somehow woke up. Then they'd need to go to the bathroom, or wanted pain medication. Yes, a few nurses would try to watch the patients while others ate their food, but it's an imperfect system. Sometimes you needed more nurses to assist you than were available, so someone got up and left their food in order to help. A completely uninterrupted break usually didn't exist for me. I know the rules are different in some union hospitals—in some places, if a nurse's break is interrupted, they get to completely start it all over again. Such was not the case where I used to work.

That's why I like to eat my hot food very hot, and my cold food very cold. It stems from my meals being interrupted for too many years and so much time spent consuming lukewarm food. Nowadays, don't expect me to ever answer a phone call during mealtime, either. Life is too short to not enjoy the food you eat.

One of my other pet peeves, or idiosyncrasies, is storing food in a dirty refrigerator. In our break room at work, we had one large, communal refrigerator which everyone shared. It was used by the nurses, the respiratory therapists, and the doctors, and it was always filled to the maximum. Sometimes you felt like you needed to push the door closed with your foot in order for it to be kept shut. I always brought my dinner in a little square lunch bag, and sometimes it was difficult to find a spare spot to squeeze it into the fridge. At the end of the shift, I always brought that bag home with me, whether I ate all the food or not. Such was not the case with all the staff members. Many of them brought their food in a brown paper bag, or whatever way the food was wrapped where it was purchased. Occasionally, food was labeled with a name and date, but usually it was not. Many left their food in the fridge in order to finish it on their next shift, and that food was occasionally pushed to the back of the refrigerator and sometimes forgotten. It wasn't until that food started growing mold or had a putrid smell that it was remembered. While sitting in the break room, sometimes we'd all gag when the refrigerator door was opened and let loose an awful odor while a nurse searched for cream for her coffee. At times, it was disgusting storing the food you wanted to consume in that kind of environment. I greatly dislike a dirty refrigerator, especially when it contains old food that needs to make a beeline to the waste management facility.

There's one other major problem with a shared refrigerator: the occasional food thief who helps himself or herself to your meal. Rarely, a staff member accidentally took a bag which they thought was theirs and brought it home with them. Sometimes they figured out they grabbed the wrong package and returned it to the ICU before they left the hospital. At other times, some sneaky individual couldn't resist a fresh sandwich or container of takeout food that looked and smelled tasty. We did not closely monitor the breakroom while we were working, and a multitude of staff had access to it. People came and went in that room. It was usually only if we saw a non-staff person—such as a patient's family member—entering the break area that we took notice. Those were the times when we were more concerned about our personal belongings versus food that was being stored. Fortunately, we all had lockers to keep our belongings safe, and most staff utilized and kept them locked.

Taking food which doesn't belong to you is one of the unkindest things you can do to a night shift staff member. I've seen the dejected or angry look on a nurse's face when they go to eat their food and find out that it is missing. Usually, it was the middle of the night when this discovery was made, long after the time when someone would be able to order new takeout food from a restaurant. The only other option was wasting money in a vending machine. It was many years before management finally decided to staff the cafeteria for a brief time and provide a food service for night shift employees, but who wanted to pay for additional food when you already bought something you knew you were going to enjoy? Most of us worked twelve-hour shifts, and that was a long time on the job without nourishment. Of course, many of us offered a portion of our own food to the nurse or therapist who was robbed of a meal. However, it wasn't quite the same as anticipating and enjoying your own food.

We sometimes tried to guess who was cruel enough to take someone else's food. We often theorized, but could never prove anything. It could be anyone from a sanitation worker to a hungry intern who could easily take the food and hide it in the on-call room which was located nearby. I highly doubted that a nurse stole another colleague's food, but it was possible. Since we didn't have hidden cameras, we never solved those mysterious food disappearances. Fortunately, no one ever rummaged through my lunch bag containing homemade food. Maybe they did, but what I cooked probably didn't look appealing, so they left it alone—which was fine with me.

Whether it's food or a nurse's belongings, keep your paws to yourself. If it doesn't belong to you, don't take it. And if you're really that hungry, ask for help, because the generosity of people might surprise you.

Chargette

One of the duties that followed me from our original ICU to the second floor was the role of "charge nurse." Being responsible for the ICU at night was never something I requested. I always felt as if this leadership role was forced upon me; I was never given a choice whether I wanted it or not. Honestly, I never recall ever enjoying this function. The only part of it that ever brought me pleasure was when I looked at my paycheck at the end of the year. Earning an extra $1.25 an hour for my role as charge nurse, I'd amass approximately an additional $1600 annually. Currently, I was employed part time and in charge almost every night I worked. Whenever I walked into the ICU at the start of my shift and looked on our assignment sheet, I dreaded seeing the letters "CHG" next to my name.

I distinctly remember the first time I was given the

duty as charge nurse; it was a complete and utter shock to me. Walking in to work as usual, a few minutes before the start of my shift, I was handed a blank sheet of paper.

"You're in charge tonight. You need to make out the assignment."

I don't know whose idea this was, but it was beyond a cruel joke. They hadn't given me any advance notice that this was going to be sprung on me that night. If I had been forewarned, I would have arrived at work much earlier. After receiving a quick report from the previous charge nurse, they expected me to make an adequate assignment which was mostly fair to everyone on duty. Both the evening and night shift nurses crowded around me, waiting for the assignments to be determined. No one could start giving anyone else a change of shift report until the assignment was posted. With each passing minute, the nurses were becoming more and more impatient. I'd complete the assignment, and then I'd hear someone say, "You can't possibly put those two patients together," or, "No, that pairing of patients isn't fair, either." Working with a pencil, I kept erasing and making changes until there was a hole rubbed through the paper. Finally, someone grabbed the paper from me and posted an assignment that had already been tentatively made. I felt like a complete failure and was made to look foolish, unable to complete the task that was harshly and unexpectedly thrown at me. That was unfortunately my first, but not the last time I was the charge nurse, otherwise known as the "Chargette."

Yes, I understood that someone needed to be assigned this duty. It was also part of the process of becoming a senior staff member. Everyone eventually needed the experience of learning charge responsibilities in order to be able to perform this duty, and to gain appreciation for the role. But I had no aspirations to ever become a supervisor or manager. I also felt as though I was given this additional work more often than other staff members. As I was rarely being told I was doing a fantastic job as the charge nurse, I didn't view it as a compliment that I seemed to always be given this role. Instead, I felt my colleagues didn't want the hassles that were part of this job, so they avoided it.

Some of the responsibilities included making out patient assignments for the next shift and trying to find a nurse to fill a vacancy if a staff member called out sick. The charge nurse had to know what was generally happening with all of the patients in order to give a brief report to the night supervisor. This report helped determine the acuity of the unit and how many staff members were kept on duty for the following shift. Often it was a game of how skillfully you could convince the supervisor that you needed all your staff and that no one should be "floated" to work in a different critical care area. Usually, it didn't appear to matter how well you pleaded your case to the supervisor— staff was moved, in what was possibly a premeditated plan. Regardless, when the day shift nurses arrived at work, they were not thrilled when they looked at the assignments and saw they were working short staffed.

Other nurses were displeased that they were assigned as charge nurse, had to precept a new nurse, or were going to receive the first admission of the day. I tried not to take their comments personally. They had no idea how much I agonized over making the best and fairest assignments possible, despite what any of them thought.

I need to add and clarify that there were a few supervisors with whom it was a pleasure working. They genuinely cared about the staff in the hospital and made many difficult decisions. Weighing the needs of all the departments, they were very diplomatic and professional when staffing determinations were made. Some of my favorite supervisors took the time to speak with me when they knew I was feeling stressed or dejected. They offered emotional support after a patient died during a code, acknowledging that we tried our best, despite the results. We were thanked when we expediently accepted new admissions to our unit, swiftly providing the skilled care a person needed. Most important of all, some of the supervisors commiserated with me when I occasionally expressed my frustrations with being in charge.

During those times, they said things to me such as, "Sometimes it's a thankless duty," or, "You often have to make unpopular decisions and you can't make everyone happy. Giving people bad news that they don't want to hear, especially if it means the team is going to be working short staffed, isn't easy. It bothers you so much because you care. Some things are beyond your control, and you're doing a great job." Words such as those usually made me feel better for a while.

Fortunately, no major incidents happened when I was in charge, as far as I can recall. Not having to ever progress through the chain of command and call upper management because of some type of catastrophe was a blessing. If I did have any charge nurse issues at night, discussing the problems could wait until my manager arrived at work in the morning.

But it seemed as if I was becoming more anxious or downcast each time I worked. Why was I becoming so unhappy with the job? Why was I starting to get so many headaches? Without realizing it, I was beginning to get burned out from the job, and being in charge most nights was not helping my situation. The role of "Chargette" was one more reason why I thought I wanted a different job.

Fifty-Five

One night at work, when I looked around at my colleagues who were on duty with me, I came to a sudden realization: I had the most seniority in the ICU compared to the people with whom I was working. No, I was not the oldest nurse working—there were a couple other nurses working with me who probably had more overall ICU experience, but not within the hospital where we currently worked. I supposed that was why, once again, I was "in charge" of the unit for the night.

Our ICU had undergone some changes in recent months and years. Many reasons existed for those changes, but they were all related to staffing issues. Since the new ICU was built and opened, we needed to recruit more staff. Nurses who had once worked on the upper floors joined us, and some of them finally completed their weeks of ICU orientation. Other nurses were contracted from local agencies or were "traveler" nurses. Certainly, most of them were competent and had ICU skills, but not every ICU across the country adhered to the same protocols. The way medications were titrated, for example, may have been different in Florida than it was in Rhode Island. Even between Rhode Island hospitals, policies could be very different. Even though these nurses functioned on their own licenses, I still felt responsible to make sure they didn't overstep boundaries in the hospital where I was employed.

The revolving door of new ICU staff seemed to continue for quite a while. What compounded this problem was the fact that management hired some very ambitious employees. Several nurses were striving to become a future PA or Certified Registered Nurse Anesthetist (CRNA); these nurses wanted an ICU job only to acquire a year of critical care experience so they could apply for advanced degree education. Once the minimum amount of experience they needed was obtained, they quit and never returned.

One of the nurses I worked with at that time who didn't fit into any of the forementioned categories has remained vividly in my mind. Jane was an RN who had worked as a critical care nurse for many years, but temporarily left the profession in order to have children. A dedicated mother, the few months she took off turned into years away from the job. Her children were now older, either entering or continuing with college educations. She wanted some supplemental income to help pay their bills. Perhaps fifteen or twenty years had elapsed since Jane worked in critical care.

Jane was a friendly, caring person who was eager to become reacquainted with the ICU routine, but she quickly realized how much had changed in an ICU environment since she last worked in one. I could imagine how she felt. In my own experience, many things had changed in the approximately fifteen years I worked as an RN. We no longer used mercury thermometers; instead, we had temporal scanners. Drugs which were formerly utilized during cardiac arrests were replaced with newer drugs. Hardwired monitors and IV pumps were more streamlined and different. Medical equipment and practices kept evolving as the years progressed. Jane had a great deal of medical knowledge, but everything else was new to her. I witnessed her growing frustrations at work and tried to be sympathetic. Sadly, a couple of the younger nurses weren't as kind. She didn't work fast enough for their tastes, and they considered her a "dinosaur." I truly felt bad for Jane. Age fifty-five is certainly not old, and she was an intelligent person. Within a brief period of time, she resigned from the ICU. She felt she might be better suited for a different department or specialty, as the critical care unit was not what she remembered or expected.

I occasionally wondered if I might become "Jane" someday. *Will a time come in my life when I leave the profession and am unsuccessfully able to return to it? Will younger nurses look at me and laugh behind my back because they think I'm not as efficient at the job as they are? Will I lose my skills or be unable to make the transition to using new equipment? Will I give up from sheer frustration with all the changes in the medical field, including electronic charting?* Eventually, I did get answers to my own questions.

I want to conclude by saying that Jane was probably the exception, not the norm. Not everyone who leaves the profession and wants to return has difficulty such as she did. There are many nurses who are older than Jane who successfully work well into their 60s, possibly even longer than that. Young or old, a nurse should not be judged solely by her age.

Insulin
and Laxatives

It seemed there definitely was a need for our new sixteen-bed ICU, because it was almost always filled to capacity. The doctors often had to make the difficult decisions of who was ready to be discharged to another hospital area in order to make room for a more critical patient who needed our attention. Essentially, we were always busy. The more things change, the more things stayed the same. I realize that nowadays, during the COVID-19 epidemic and recent RSV cases or flu season, hospitals continue to contend with the same types of issues. Almost every available bed or stretcher in a hospital is utilized. Sometimes a patient could wait for days in the ER, or the PACU nurses would be required to look after non-surgical patients.

Busy nights made the hours of a shift fly by swiftly.

Crazy nights were pure insanity. We worked well together most of the time, but sometimes it appeared that it was an "everyone for himself" mentality. You did the best you could with your own patient and helped your colleagues when possible.

I doubt I will ever forget the night when my assignment was Rooms 15 and 16. Stationed in a corner of the unit, I knew I was going to have an extremely busy night as I listened to the change of shift report. Unafraid of hard work, I tentatively planned how I was going to organize my time in order to provide care to these two sick patients. Not wanting to waste any time, I immediately started my duties when the nursing report was completed. The first challenge I faced was the fact that both of the patients were in isolation rooms, so I needed to wear a clean paper gown and gloves every time I entered each room. I also knew my hands would be rubbed red and raw before the end of my shift due to the amount of hand washing or cleansing with alcohol-based disinfectant which was required.

Not long after this shift started, I saw the ICU team of doctors rolling their portable cart in my direction. Physician rounds used to occur only in the morning, in the past. More recently, twice-daily rounds were being performed in order to address issues on a timely basis. As the patient's nurse, I was expected to attend these rounds unless there were unusual circumstances, such as if I was unavailable because I was accompanying the patient on a trip to CT scan. Actually, I looked forward to the rounds most of the time, since it was an opportunity to provide my own input to the group of doctors. At times, when the Medical Director or a Fellow I admired was leading the rounds, it was a good educational experience for me. The more senior doctor quizzed the Interns and Residents, and I listened carefully to the questions and answers.

On this particular night, the Fellow directing his subordinates was Trevor. I was already waiting for the group to approach my direction. Trevor asked who the primary nurse for the patient in Bed 15 was, and I acknowledged that it was me. Unlike Misbah, Trevor was not my favorite Fellow. Listening to him, all I heard was "blah, blah, blah," because I was starting to tune out what he was saying. But I paid more attention when he finally got to the point where the team were going to start writing new orders for my patient. I'd have new tasks added to my duties for the night. What stood out in the group of orders was an insulin drip which was going to be initiated, and laxatives that I needed to administer. The insulin drip would involve frequent checking of blood sugar levels and titration of the medication per a new protocol which was being trialed in the ICU. The laxatives would probably act quickly, necessitating cleaning the patient frequently in order to keep him comfortable and protect his fragile skin. Being in an isolation room made these additional duties more time consuming.

After moving on to my next patient, in Bed 16, Trevor asked once again, "Who's taking care of this patient?"

I responded once more, "That's my patient, too."

Rounds on this patient started. More "blah, blah, blah" was heard before orders were written. He looked at me and said, "We're ordering an insulin drip and laxatives for this patient as well." After a brief pause, he added, "Well, you certainly have a shitty assignment tonight, don't you? Literally."

Then he laughed. Standing directly in front of me, he actually had the nerve to laugh in my face. Knowing that I would be cleaning up poop in both of those isolation rooms all night, he thought the situation was hilarious. *What a jerk.* Needless to say, I didn't think it was funny whatsoever.

The night was as bad as I knew it would be. I felt like I was a bouncing ping pong ball between the two rooms. If I wasn't cleaning feces, I was checking blood-work, or administering other medications. All the other nurses were also very busy. It was difficult recruiting the help I needed to help me turn my patients or fetch supplies I needed, since I couldn't freely enter or leave the isolation rooms. All shift long, isolation gear was frequently put on and taken off, with copious amounts of hand cleansing as well. The only saving grace was that both patients were intubated and sedated, so I could go into each room without also having to make pleasant conversation with my customers. I know I didn't sit down or take any breaks during the entire shift. It was a terrible night, and I couldn't wait for it to be over.

After the night was finished, I had a lot to think about during the drive home. Yes, I've had extremely busy shifts in the past, but this previous shift was the culmination of many unhappy nights at work. The ICU had finally taken its toll on me, and I was burned out from working there for so many years. That assignment, including Trevor's inconsiderate laughter, was the last straw. I couldn't take it anymore.

I had a few days off from work, and I spent that time looking for a new job. I wanted to remain employed in the medical profession as a nurse, but I needed a big change. I was accustomed to working night shift, so I looked for decent jobs with night hours, although they were not plentiful. Finding a potential job with an anesthesia group, I went on a job interview and was hired. It was a tremendous reduction in pay, but at the time I didn't care. I gave my manager two weeks of notice and I quit my current job, leaving the hospital in which I had worked for fourteen years.

Making that decision was a bit scary, but I felt it was the right thing to do at the time. One thoughtful manager suggested I transfer to the CVT-S unit, since I had experience taking care of cardiothoracic patients. Hospital policy had once again changed, and twelve-hour shifts were reinstituted in that unit, unlike when the new CVT-S first opened and only eight-hour shifts were available. I appreciated her suggestion but notified her that I needed a change and wanted to try something completely new in my career.

My last shift in the ICU was anticlimactic. It was just another bad night at work, where once again I was given a patient assignment which included the first admission. A cake had been bought for me, but I had little time to actually sit with my colleagues and enjoy the dessert. I was hoping that I would have had an "easier" assignment for my last shift, so I could have spent my last few hours at the hospital saying goodbye to my coworkers and reminiscing over some of the "old times" we had together. But that didn't happen. Having a conscience and a sense of duty, I was obliged to take good care of my patients up until the final moments of my last shift. It was truly surreal walking out of the hospital for what I thought was going to be the last time. I didn't smile, nor did I cry. Life moves forward, and I was determined to embrace change.

Oh Baby

My new job consisted of working in what's generally considered Rhode Island's "baby hospital." There were other hospitals in the region which had maternity wards and delivery rooms, but I was employed by the largest one in the state. Actually, I wasn't hired by the hospital but by the Anesthesia group that the hospital utilized. It would prove to be an interesting and informative experience for me

I took a rather hefty pay cut, and my new job seemed to be one suited for a tech instead of an RN. I had my share of RN duties, but it was nothing like working in critical care. But I had wanted and needed a change, right? This job certainly couldn't have been more different than what I was used to for over a decade.

I obtained patient histories from women in labor, or those who arrived in the ER and needed surgical intervention relating to gynecological issues. Mostly, I would set up an epidural, which would be inserted into a woman's back by the Anesthesiologist for pain control during labor. After the baby's birth, I removed the epidural catheter. In between those duties, I documented multiple sets of vital signs on women. Sometimes I had menial tasks, such as cleaning up the anesthesia area in the OR after a surgical case was completed. Easy enough, right? The problem was that I didn't find any true nursing satisfaction in those tasks. I soon realized that I craved to be respected and appreciated for my vast medical knowledge, and to be able to use it, not waste any talent I possessed. The job amounted to a paycheck, and that was about it. I had earnestly tried to make this new employment work out, but it was not the ideal job for me. Still hoping my feelings about the situation would eventually change, several months passed by...but I remained unhappy while employed by the anesthesia group. I eventually left the job, within a year, and returned to the hospital where I was formerly employed in Providence.

However, I didn't go back to the ICU but to the CVT-S unit, instead. The manager happened to be the same one who tried to convince me not to leave the hospital but to transfer to CVT-S. After seeing the job posted on the hospital website under the Careers section, I gave her a call. It was extremely flattering to be hired on the spot, over the phone, without a job interview. This manager had known me for many years, and knew I was capable of functioning as a nurse in the job that was available. I was going to start working there at the start of the following week.

Except for a few things, I wasn't the least bit sad when I left the anesthesia job. One event I felt I would miss a little bit was watching a baby being born. Never having given birth to an infant of my own, it was an eye-opening experience watching women go through the process of labor and delivery. My favorite part of the job was after a baby was delivered and the mother and family member present looked so happy. I loved being a part of that moment, and happily took photos of them with their phone or camera. Since I enjoyed amateur photography as a hobby, I thought the photos I took might be a little better than random snapshots. However, I don't think it was necessarily the quality of the photos that the family cared about but the fact that those special moments were captured in a timely fashion.

The labor and delivery nurses were also fantastic. They performed their jobs well and were able to react quickly and bring a woman in labor swiftly to the OR if a crisis occurred with either the mother or baby. Even though they only knew me for nine months, on my final day of work I was presented with a huge food buffet which we all enjoyed. I was also given a lovely card which many of them signed, and their farewell wishes were greatly appreciated.

My "baby job" also taught me a few things which were useful in the future. Every job, whether you liked it or not, was a learning opportunity. I've often said that any form of education is not wasted time.

When I started that job, I was thrust into the role of being the "anesthesia nurse" on duty. One of my roles was to obtain IV access or draw blood if one of the labor and delivery nurses was not successful in those tasks. Usually, they were extremely good with these duties, and only asked for help if they had difficulty with a patient's veins. Suddenly, I was supposed to be an expert in this area. Honestly, I rarely had to draw blood or insert an IV in a patient in the past. I was accustomed to caring for ICU patients who had an arterial line, which was an extremely easy way to draw blood. Most of them also had central lines which allowed me to either administer medications or obtain blood. Those were things I took for granted until I was required to place an IV in an alert and uncomfortable woman in labor. Initially, I thought my first successful attempts at being able to insert a functioning IV were sheer luck. Then, as I started overcoming my hesitancy, that skill improved. It came to the point where I started enjoying the challenge of looking for suitable veins in a person's arm. By the time I quit working at the baby hospital, I was very proficient at inserting IVs. It was a learned skill which was extremely useful when I worked in CVT-S. In that department, phlebotomy was rarely utilized; it was expected that we draw our own blood. We also needed to insert new IVs in our patients after their central lines were discontinued and they transitioned to the step-down unit. Whether they were male or female, many of them were elderly with poor veins. The arms of those patients were also still edematous after surgery, which often added to the difficulty of accessing an adequate vein. It was pleasurable hearing a patient say to me, "I wish they had asked you to draw my blood or place that IV first, because you easily got the needle in with only one attempt."

The most important thing I learned from my anesthesia assistant job, however, was something unrelated to any skill I could ever develop. That job taught me that I shouldn't ever fear stepping out of my "comfort zone" and try something new. Many of us fear failure or change. Those things are usually inevitable at some point as we go through life. We grow and mature through various experiences, especially the negative ones. Leaving one hospital and briefly working in another one showed me that I could try a different department and then come back to something familiar if that's what I wanted. That job helped me reconsider what type of employment truly made me happy.

Perky

Working once again with open heart surgical patients felt like coming back home to myself. Although the physical surroundings had changed, I easily remembered the patient care and nightly routines. A few of the staff were new to me, but I mostly saw familiar faces, which made me very happy. My orientation period was extremely brief, then I was once again taking full care of my own assigned patients.

The age range of our surgical patient population varied, but they were always adults. As technology and healthcare advanced, it seemed we were taking care of older and older adults. Who would have imagined that someone in their 80s or 90s could undergo open heart surgery, or even minimally invasive surgical heart procedures? I learned not to completely rely on someone's age to determine the level of their health. Sometimes

I found that a very elderly woman did extremely well after surgery while a man much younger than myself appeared to be ancient and made poor post-surgical progress. Everyone is unique and needs to be treated as an individual.

Upon admitting a patient from the OR one evening, I saw nothing unusual about her immediate postop care. No extremes in vital signs or lab values—it was routine. Once it appeared that a patient was going to remain fairly stable, most of the nurses caring for this type of person started performing physical care such as bathing and turning the individual side to side. Repositioning facilitated the chest tubes to drain accumulated body fluids and it also gave us a chance to inspect skin and prevent tissue breakdown. We changed the sheets, which may also be stained with antiseptic solution or blood. Doing all of these things before the patient started waking up from anesthesia medicine made it easier for them as well as the nurses. Working swiftly, usually two nurses performed these tasks together.

Upon enlisting Allissa's help to perform my patient's bath, we decided we'd take care of this patient first, then we planned to go to her patient's room and do the same thing. Donning gloves and obtaining antiseptic cloths and towels, we each stood on opposite sides of the bed and started cleaning. We worked carefully around the medical equipment attached to the patient. Her torso was uncovered while we washed.

Allissa looked up at me and asked, "How old is she, anyhow?" Looking at her wristband, I told her the

Karen, MaryAnn, and Bethany, CVT-S and e-ICU friends

patient's age, which was in her late 70s. Totally amazed and looking at the woman, she pointed to her chest, stating, "Wow, she certainly got her money's worth when she had her breasts augmented. That's one fantastic big boob job. She's that old and they're still not sagging? I wish mine were that perky."

I had to agree; the woman's breasts were rather large, firm, and upright. It was unusual for our clientele of elderly women patients to have anatomy that looked that way.

As we continued to cleanse the patient, the mystery of her large breasts was soon revealed. Upon touching the skin around her upper chest and neck, we realized that she had extensive subcutaneous emphysema. The crepitus, which is air trapped under the skin and feels like crackling Rice Krispy cereal when you touch it, was developing and extending. There was likely an issue with her chest tube, so we called the cardiac physician assistant to the bedside, notifying him of the subcutaneous emphysema. After evaluating the patient and ensuring proper placement of the chest tube with X-rays, the assistante determined she required a little extra care. After monitoring and documenting the extent of the crepitus, it was eventually completely resolved before she was discharged from the ICU. I don't believe that elderly woman ever realized that, temporarily, she had enormous breasts which easily could have rivaled those of any very well-endowed movie star.

Generator

Owning a generator certainly comes in handy when the power goes out where you live. It doesn't seem to matter what region of the country you call home—power failure can happen anywhere and for various reasons. Rolling blackouts may be scheduled in places such as California when power demand is high. In areas prone to tornadoes or flooding, power loss sometimes happens for long periods of time after a severe storm. In the Northeast, we are occasionally hit with damaging blizzards. Sometimes, it's something as simple as when a car hits a telephone pole during an auto accident which causes a power failure. When the electricity goes out, it could be several hours or multiple days before it is restored.

When Wayne and I decided to buy a piece of property in a rural area of RI, our realtor gave us a piece of advice which we followed. The realtor told us, "If you're going to build a house and live out here, the first thing you should do is buy a generator. You're surrounded by a lot of trees which can fall on power lines during a storm. If you lose electricity, you're probably not going to get it back right away. Let's face it: the more populated areas of the state will get electricity back before you do. The needs of the many outweigh the needs of the few."

And he certainly was correct in what he said. Fortunately, we haven't lost power during a snowstorm. Rather, it's been during hurricane season in autumn when our electricity has gone out. The trees, still clinging to their leaves, act as big sails when the wind blows. If the wind is forceful, branches break or trees get uprooted. These sometimes make contact and cause the electrical lines to come down to the ground. That's what happened one year during a hurricane in the month of September.

Upon arriving at work after the storm was over, I saw that the hospital was functioning normally. A backup generator was on standby, but it wasn't needed during that particular storm. But there were several new patients in the hospital who needed access to our electrical power. They had medical conditions of varying degrees, but had no electricity in their homes which could run vital lifesaving equipment. I was dumbfounded that someone who was so dependent on a piece of medical equipment wouldn't have a backup generator for an emergency situation. But it was pointed out to me that some of these customers may live in an apartment building, not necessarily their own house. Their solution to electrical problems was to call the fire department or 911, at which point an ambulance would transport them to the hospital. They would be cared for as patients until power was restored to where they lived.

I was assigned to two patients that night at work. One was a relatively fresh postop cardiac patient, and the other was a gentleman who was in the ICU because he was ventilator dependent at night. The patient who needed the ventilator had a tracheostomy, but could talk and eat during the day. Through use of what's called a Passy-Muir valve, this cap was placed over the tracheostomy and allowed a person to audibly speak. He was supposed to be my "easy" patient, residing at the "hotel hospital" for a day or two. He had the room with the nicest view of the city, access to a TV, and meals were also provided for him. There shouldn't have been much that he needed from me except administration of his medication and routine checks. Remember: he was living at home fairly independently, and was only admitted to the hospital because of his need for access to electricity to run his ventilator at night while he slept.

This patient was certainly not an "easy" one for me. He was demanding and used up a lot of time which should have been directed toward care of my other patient. Every time he put on his call light, I had to stop what I was doing with my sicker patient and check on him. We didn't have nurses' aides in our unit to take care of things like that which didn't necessarily require an RN's expertise. Walking up and down the hallway numerous times, I realized I was in for an extremely long night. For the most part, the patient was lonely and wanted company. I was initially sympathetic toward his needs, but I was unable to spend the entire shift babysitting him the way he wanted. He was selfish and unrealistic, even after I explained to him that I couldn't spend all night with him because my other patient was very sick and needed my care.

It didn't matter what I said. He started shouting in order to get my attention when I wasn't in his room. Not yelling because he was confused—he was manipulative and knew exactly what he was saying. My blood was slowly beginning to boil with each word that came out of his mouth. I couldn't wait for the night to be over. What made me so mad? It was all the blasphemy that he was spewing. Anyone who knew me very well was aware that I despised it when someone casually and irreverently threw God's or Jesus' name around. He was continually saying things like, "Oh God! Oh God! Help me, Jesus! Oh, help me, Jesus!" Perhaps I was completely wrong, but I truly didn't think he was sincerely praying or asking God for help. It was attention-seeking behavior, and I was relieved when he was finally placed on the ventilator for the night and stopped talking for a while.

The span of silence from this guest patient was short lived, because he didn't sleep for very long. He banged his call light on the siderail of his bed to let me know he was awake and wanted to be taken off the ventilator to get ready for breakfast. Breakfast was not going to be served for another few hours, but he didn't want to try to go back to sleep. If we didn't take him off the ventilator as demanded, he was simply going to remove the tubing himself, causing the machine to alarm loudly. Once again, he started yelling. The few hours of rest he obtained had not changed his attitude. This time, his language was more specific.

He was saying, "Oh God, let me die! Let me die, God! Oh, Jesus! Oh, Jesus! Come get me, Jesus!"

Despite spending more time with him and helping him get bathed in the morning, the ranting and rambling never stopped. I was going to suggest to the next nurse and his doctor that this patient gets a psychiatric consult before going home. We weren't going to start making changes to his medication in the middle of the night because he was only a short-term boarder in CVT. But his mental status and medications may have needed to be evaluated by a psychiatrist at some point.

Happily, the end of my shift had almost arrived, and I was finishing my duties in the tracheostomy patient's room. Totally disgusted by his outbursts, I performed one final deed for him before I departed his room. It was early Sunday morning, and I put the TV on for him. Not asking him what he wanted to watch, I found a TV channel which was airing a Christian church mass. *Since you're calling out to God and Jesus so much, I'll find them on TV for you. If you're sincere in what you're saying, you might find comfort in what you're watching. Otherwise, I don't care if you don't want to watch Catholic mass; you're stuck with it now. That's what you get for being a blaspheming fraud.* His fat, stubby little fingers easily found the button to call the nurse on the remote control, but he didn't seem to have the dexterity to change the TV channel, or its volume. I walked out of his room and hoped I wouldn't have him again as a patient when I came back to work in a couple of days.

When I returned to work on Tuesday, the patient I disliked wasn't there any longer. I casually inquired about him, saying, "He must have gotten his electricity back faster than most people."

One of the nurses replied, "Actually, he died later in the day on Sunday."

I was flabbergasted. I didn't have much to say about it and didn't ask what actually happened to him. *Maybe he really knew he was going to die and wanted to see Jesus. Perhaps I did him a favor by tuning his TV to a Godly church service.*

It's one of many things to which I'll never have an answer.

Follow the Trail

Checking the assignment sheet after walking into CVT-S, I saw the dreaded word "float" next to my name. The charge nurse knew how I would feel about it, and said, "It's only for four hours, then you'll come back here." Those words weren't much consolation to me.

Floating consisted of going to a different hospital department for a specific number of hours to help them if your unit was overstaffed. We kept a list of the dates and names of nurses who floated in order to assign this duty fairly. No one volunteered to float or wanted this task more than was absolutely necessary. Tonight, it was my turn. Occasionally, someone was offered time off and could stay home, but the hospital seemed to be perpetually short staffed in most departments, and we were obliged to help them. Sometimes CVT didn't have a lot of patients as the holidays approached. Either patients didn't want to undergo elective surgery at those times, or the surgeons were on vacation. Policy changed in later years, and nurses were only required to float between critical care areas. However, at the moment, we were often sent to work on general medical wards and were usually given a patient assignment.

Working on the medical wards versus in the critical care areas is like comparing apples to oranges, in my opinion. Nurses on the floors didn't always have much sympathy for the ICU nurse floaters. The general sentiment sometimes seemed to be, "Oh, poor you. You only take care of one or two patients. See what it's like to be responsible for six to eight patients or more. We work our butts off."

There is no denying that nurses work very hard, and a large patient caseload is not easy. ICU nurses acknowledge that being a nurse on the upstairs wards could be very difficult. Those floor nurses forget that was where most of the critical care nurses started working early in their careers. We remember what it was like, which is why we love working in the ICU. But being employed in an ICU isn't exactly a picnic in the park, either. We take care of the sickest, most unstable people in the hospital, which isn't easy. It's usually not until one of the floor nurses decides to transfer and accept a job in the ICU that he or she understands what our job truly entails.

Enough said about that.

After walking up to the fourth floor, I was given a six-patient assignment for the few hours I'd be working there. I would have preferred to function as a nurses' aide, helping all of the RNs in whatever way they needed assistance. Taking a full assignment for only four hours didn't leave much time to complete all of the required duties before returning back to CVT-S. The other floor nurses would have all night long to complete their charting. I had to care for the patients, chart, give a sign-out report, and then rush back down to CVT-S to receive report on two critical care patients. It certainly wasn't my ideal type of work shift.

The patients for whom I was caring on the fourth floor were pleasant enough. I rushed from one room to the next, taking vital signs, performing brief assessments, and handing out medication. It somewhat brought back memories of working in Worcester. Next, I had to start rounds again, preparing all my patients for bedtime. Everyone needed to use the bathroom in one way or another. Many of my ICU patients had urinary catheters, or they were connected to so many IVs or other crucial equipment that they were unable to walk to the bathroom. If they were able to get out of bed, a bedside commode or urinal was what they were allowed to use. Walking someone to the bathroom was different than what I had become accustomed to for the past several years. It seemed simple enough.

Wrong. I had to locate a walker for one patient, because he looked like he might be a little unsteady on his feet and shuffled along. Another patient needed to talk less and walk more, since he kept stopping because he wanted to tell me something. I am proof that a person can walk and talk at the same time, and encouraged him to do the same.

Additionally, my third patient told me she needed to use the bathroom "NOW." She felt the urgent need to have a bowel movement. Knowing that locating a bedside commode would take much longer than walking her to the bathroom, I decided to assist her with ambulation to the toilet. In that patient's room, her bed was the one closest to the window. Oh, how I wished her bed was the one nearer to the bathroom, but it wasn't. After putting the little non-skid slipper socks on her feet, I helped her stand and she was preparing to start walking to the toilet.

Before moving a step, she exclaimed, "Wait a minute, it's coming out!"

WAIT? No, lady, we need to get to the bathroom NOW.

In one swift movement, she turned and sat on the windowsill, which actually was the heating radiator for the individual room. I was working in one of the older parts of the hospital, and this vented heater was still utilized. Fortunately, it was warm but not hot, so she didn't get burned. However, she pooped a little into the slatted top of the heater. Unable to leave her there, I encouraged her to try to make it to the bathroom to finish her toileting needs. *Bad idea.* With each step she took, diarrhea came squirting out of her rear end. There was literally a trail of shit leading from the window to the bathroom. Walking behind her, I straddled the line of fecal material, attempting to avoid getting any of it on my clothes or shoes. We safely made it to the toilet. It was at this time that I heard one of the night supervisors calling my name.

"Ann, are you in there? Just want to check on how you're doing."

It was Carol, one of my favorite supervisors. Stopping in the doorway before entering the patient's room, she saw the line of poop on the floor.

"Oh, my" was all she said. She quickly left to gather many towels for me; I bet she emptied the entire linen cart. While helping me clean up my patient as well as the floor, she said, "Oh, Ann, I'm so sorry...."

She knew my floating experience was terrible that night, and expressed her empathy. Sympathy was probably needed more for the maintenance person who had to inspect the internal elements of the heater, which we were unable to clean. Long after I left the fourth floor, I wondered how much that specific room stunk from the combination of diarrhea on a warm heating device. I almost wouldn't have believed what happened in that room if I hadn't witnessed it for myself.

Husbands and Wives

Never wanting to offend anyone, I try to think carefully about what I'm going to say before the words come out of my mouth. On a few occasions, however, I know I've definitely said the wrong thing to a patient, and I was greatly embarrassed because of it. Once, I walked into a patient's room to offer assistance because I knew their nurse was still receiving the change of shift report.

Not knowing anything about the patient, I innocently asked, "May I help you, sir?"

The patient was very irate with me and immediately responded, "I'm a *woman!*"

Ooops. I offered my sincerest apologies without trying to insert my foot further into my mouth. Fortunately, she wasn't my own patient, and I avoided that room like the plague for the remainder of the night. I'm not a beautiful person with delicate feminine features, either. Certainly, sitting in a hospital bed without makeup or jewelry, someone may make the same mistake in my room someday, if I'm ever a patient. That experience taught me to solely ask a person, "May I help you?"

While working on CVT-S, I once again said the wrong thing to a patient and his family. At the start of my shift, I'd always go into my patient's room and introduce myself as their nurse. It was usually nice meeting their family, if they were also present. Sometimes they voluntarily introduced themselves first, stating something such as, "This is my husband and my oldest child," or, "This is my best friend; my spouse died years ago." Those were easy introductions, and that method worked well.

I made a mistake one night which I think is also probably made in a variety of ways, more often than we realize. Walking into my surgical patient's room, I said hello to him. I had taken care of him the previous night, so there was no need for me to reintroduce myself to him. However, he had a visitor, and told me she was a family member. I turned to the young woman and said, "Pleased to meet you, you must be his daughter." I regretted the words as soon as they left my mouth—I could tell I said something wrong by her hesitation and weak smile.

She corrected me, saying, "Actually, I'm his wife."

Dumb, dumb, dumb. If I could have crawled under the bed and disappeared, I wouldn't have hesitated. What more could I say, except, "Sorry, my mistake," without making the situation worse?

AACN Certification Corporation

hereby grants

CCRN.

status to

Ann M. Watt

in recognition of the successful completion
of all requirements for Certification in

Adult Critical-Care Nursing

Certified through:
February 28, 2010

Rebecca E. Long

Rebecca E. Long, RN, MS, CCRN, CMSRN
Chair, AACN Certification Corporation Board of Directors

CCRN Certificate

The patient's wife was *very* young and beautiful. I'm terrible at guessing a person's age, but I estimate that she was easily more than twenty years younger than her husband. They could have been playing a joke on me, but they weren't. I don't begrudge him at all for being able to find such a youthful and attractive woman who is now his wife. Many men probably dream of having a wife who looks like her. I'm sure I'm not the first person who misidentified her relationship with her husband, but that didn't make me feel any better. I made an assumption, and said something stupid. Yet another lesson learned. Now, when I inquire as to the relationship between a visitor and a patient, I merely ask, "And you are?" Giving someone the opportunity to answer that question is the safest option when you're not quite sure how people are related. Thankfully, I never made that mistake again.

White Snow
and Dove

Some people in New England hope for a mild winter, and others prefer lots of snow. Needless to say, the people who operate ski resorts want to have cold and snowy weather for their seasonal industry. Children want a "snow day" off from school and also enjoy skiing or sledding. Others escape the region entirely; these "snowbirds" head south for the winter months. Some of us remain where we live and hope for a temperate winter, especially when we have to manually clear snow from our property or are forced to drive in foul weather. Personally, I don't mind the snow, but I always hope it's not snowing when I have to head in to work. Snow makes my commute much longer, especially if the wind is fiercely blowing, creating blinding driving conditions.

It's inexcusable for a nurse to not arrive at work because of a snowstorm. You learn very early in your career that you are expected to be present for your shift, regardless of the weather conditions. Even if that involves arriving hours earlier before a storm hits, that is what you do. Nurses often arrive at work with extra food and clothing during storms. Just because you make it in safely to work doesn't mean that you will be able to leave when your shift is over. Sometimes too much snow accumulates to allow you to safely depart the hospital, or you may be mandated to stay for an additional shift because your relief doesn't show up or is late.

I invested in a car with all-wheel drive as soon as I could afford the make and model I wanted. Even though I lived in Rhode Island, which is known as the "Ocean State," many of the roads are not flat. However, it didn't really matter where you lived in the state. Your vehicle still had to climb a steep street in order to reach the hospital, which was located at the top of a hill. You would think that the streets surrounding a hospital would be some of the first ones to be plowed or sanded during a winter storm, but that wasn't the case. I was not usually worried about my own car's capabilities or my driving skills; it was other drivers which caused me concern. Being behind a vehicle which had no traction and was sliding backward toward my car was a little unnerving at times. Trying to drive around a slightly out-of-control vehicle was sketchy, at best.

I really liked my new car and didn't want it

damaged during foul winter weather, so I drove like a careful old lady when there was snow on the road. My acquaintances laughed when I told them how cautiously I drove in stormy conditions, because they considered me a speed demon. But it was true.

Anticipating a major storm on a night I was scheduled to work, I left my home quite early in order to make it to the hospital on time. It was already beginning to snow, and the weather was forecast to be more severe at the time I usually left my house and began my commute. Wanting to avoid the worsening conditions, I was making the wisest decision possible. After arriving at my job with plenty of time to spare before my shift started, I planned on having a leisurely cup of coffee in the break room. But when I walked into CVT-S, that wasn't destined to happen.

Walking through the automatic doors to the unit, it looked like controlled chaos. A patient had recently arrived from the OR after having open heart surgery. There was a multitude of staff still in his room because the patient was very ill. I saw on the assignment sheet that this was going to be my solitary patient for the night. Nancy, who was presently his day shift nurse, said something such as, "Feel free to jump right in." After quickly putting my belongings away and badging in for the shift, I joined her in that patient's room. Working together, we untangled IV lines, hung medication and blood, and managed other equipment. She was giving me a verbal report as we worked in the room, attempting to stabilize the patient. It was always exciting for me to take care of those fresh post-op patients, and it was immensely satisfying seeing the progress that was made in their condition over the course of a shift. Sometimes advancement was extremely slow, and at other times it was swift. The other staff members had left to take care of their own patients, so just Nancy and I were caring for this patient. It was now nearly change-of-shift time, and everyone else had things they needed to do before they departed and went home. The nurse with whom I was closely working thanked me profusely for arriving at the hospital and starting my shift as early as I did. I told her I wasn't doing anything special, and I couldn't sit back and not offer to help, especially since I knew this was going to be my patient overnight. Regardless, she was very appreciative of my actions.

The patient's condition slowly improved overnight, and it was an intense shift for me. Time passed rather swiftly when you were busy, and the shift was over in what seemed like an instant. When Nancy returned in the morning, she was once again going to be his nurse. What a difference twelve hours made. She was happy to see him looking better and thanked me one more time for helping her out last evening. I was coming back to work for another night shift, and would have further opportunity to see this patient, continuing his care.

When I returned to work, I was greeted by the day shift nurse, Nancy. Our patient was continuing to improve, which was always good news. Before she gave me a report outside of the patient's room, she retrieved

Dove ornament

a small package and handed it to me. On her lunch break that day, she bought me a present in the hospital gift shop. Yet again, she thanked me for coming to work early yesterday. It wasn't necessary for her to buy me anything, but it was greatly appreciated. The gift was a beautiful white dove Christmas ornament which was embellished with a few faux diamonds. Attached was a ribbon which had "peace on earth" written on it. Every year since that day, I have hung it on my annual Christmas tree. It's a treasured ornament and a wonderful reminder of the nurse who gave it to me, a job I enjoyed, and that snowy day.

Gourmet Meals

Regardless of what kind of food a person is served, most patients love complaining about hospital food. They say it's too bland, or too spicy. It's too hot or cold, or the texture is mush. The sandwiches are dry or you can strip paint with the decaf coffee. Blah, blah, blah. Sometimes people are simply miserable and love to complain.

Hospital food has made great improvements over the years. Dietetic, low fat, and low sugar food is not as it used to be. I remember when my father, who had severe cardiac disease from prolonged smoking, was forced to alter his diet. Low-fat cheese and yogurt used to be horrible, but now I enjoy both of those foods. Even generic canned vegetables are much better quality than they were in previous years. Hospital food certainly cannot compete with a delicious home-cooked meal, but it has its function.

If a patient has stomach issues, it's unrealistic for them to be served solid food. They are started with simple items, such as Jell-O and ginger ale. Food progression is made after you can tolerate those kinds of clear liquids. A patient who has diabetic issues isn't going to receive food loaded with sugar. It's amazing how well-controlled someone's glucose level may be in a hospital. That's because their diet is restricted and the patient is not consuming all the food they probably shouldn't be eating at home.

Other patients, after surgery, don't have the same sense of taste that they normally do. I found this to be true with our clientele of post-op cardiac patients in CVT-S. There is something about receiving anesthesia medication which appears to temporarily alter a person's sense of taste. They don't enjoy food the way they normally do. Of course, receiving antibiotics and generally feeling lousy after having your sternum cut open probably also contribute to having a poor appetite. Families, however, have to learn these things the hard way.

Sometimes a family member is appalled at what is being served to their loved one when the patient is finally allowed to eat. The spouse may look at the meal tray and say, "That's disgusting, I wouldn't serve that to my dog. I'm going to go home and cook you a proper meal." Fortunately, I mostly didn't have to deal with comments such as that. The start of my shift was at the extreme end of dinner mealtime, and night shift ended before breakfast was served. If a dinner tray and family were still lingering when I arrived at work, they were usually both escorted out of the room so I could perform my initial assessment and administer medications. Any family who complained about the meals and said they were going to bring in their own food for the patient was not prevented from doing so. *Knock yourself out. Cook up a storm if it makes you happy.* But I knew what the results would be, because it was almost always the same with every patient who was brought a home-cooked meal.

I've seen a lot of very appealing food brought to patients in the ICU. Rhode Island certainly has a lot of phenomenal cooks who make traditional Italian meals, as well as many other regional favorites. I could have easily eaten any of those meals, inhaling them with record speed. But they were brought for the patients, and stored in a separate refrigerator for them. There was a microwave, as well, to heat up the meals at a later time if a patient became hungry. But over and over, I witnessed the same thing with various food. Something such as a big piece of lasagna was plopped on a plate in front of a patient by a family member or friend. The patient took one bite, then was unable to eat any more of it. Sure, they may have craved their favorite food, but they couldn't eat it when presented with it. Occasionally, I heard a wife lamenting, "But you *love* lasagna. I spent hours cooking it just for you!" Regardless of how much he wanted to, the patient couldn't choke down another bite. When the food cooled down, we placed it back in its portable container and returned it to the communal patient refrigerator.

"Maybe he'll be able to eat some of it tomorrow," I consoled the wife. Of course, they usually never ended up consuming the home-cooked meal, and it was thrown out. I disliked wasting food, but after a patient had his fork or hands in his food, no one else dared touch it.

I do have to mention that once in a while, there is an exception to the rule. And I have to ask myself, which is actually worse: the patient who doesn't eat the homemade meal, or the patient who devours the cheesy, buttery, fat-laden food after they've had quadruple bypass heart surgery? No worries—I'll see you again, Mr. Big Appetite, in another five or ten years. That's what keeps our department in business.

Yes, I do mention to patients the benefits of healthy eating and exercise while performing discharge teaching. I actually do want them to remain well and not become repeat customers. But the wheel is not going to be reinvented, and patients will do whatever they want to do once they get home. Some of them heed counseling on healthy habits, and others do not. Bon appétit.

It's a Small State

When I was first dating my future husband, one thing always amazed me. Wherever we went, he always ran into someone he knew and stopped to chat with them for a few minutes. I was astounded by people who he remembered and saw from high school, college, work, or his neighborhood. Welcome to Rhode Island; it's a small state.

I wondered if I would ever take care of a patient who I knew outside of the hospital. Despite being the smallest state in our nation, Rhode Island had at least nine hospitals. That seemed like a lot to me for our area, but they each had a function. Eventually, I did care for a few people I recognized. On one particular night, I didn't know the patient, but I recognized a couple of her family members.

It was my turn to float again, but thankfully it was to CCU and not to the floors. My assignment consisted of what I considered an "easy" patient and also a person who was dying. The dying patient was made CMO status, and the family was waiting for her to pass away, which would likely be sometime during the course of the night. I didn't mind taking care of someone on the verge of death, but it was an assignment which a few of my colleagues did not like. Some might consider it mentally draining, or might have felt uncomfortable with the amount of grieving family members who were sometimes present. I felt like I had this type of assignment more than most nurses, and I was probably considered the "Death Angel" nurse. In the past, my parents had dragged me to more funerals than a child should ever attend. Dealing with the topic or reality of death doesn't bother me much now that I'm an adult.

A couple of my dying patient's family members recognized me. After giving it a moment's thought, I realized that they lived in the same small town as me, and could be considered "neighbors." They knew the street and house where I lived, and it was easy talking with them about some things we had in common. Trying my best to comfort them and make a difficult situation a little less painful, I attended to their few needs or requests. I did for them what I would have done for any patient and family in a similar situation. I knew how I'd want my family treated if our roles were reversed, so that's how I tried to care for others. But I still didn't think I was doing anything particularly special. My patient peacefully died during the course of the night, in the early morning hours.

A few days later, on my night off, the doorbell rang at my house. Standing at the door was the granddaughter of my recently deceased patient. In her hands was a gift bag with a few items inside of it, and she handed it to me.

"My mom wanted you to know how much she appreciated you taking care of her mother."

I was stunned, and expressed my own appreciation for the personal gift before she departed. Inside the bag was a large brand-name jar candle, as well as a gorgeous hummingbird feeder and small bird nesting basket. We had discussed hummingbirds among other things while we waited for her mother to die. The gift was extremely thoughtful and totally unexpected.

Occasionally, our customers or their family wrote a single thank-you card to the staff who cared for them. A handwritten note is always appreciated, and it doesn't have to be lengthy. Taking the time to make that simple yet special gesture reminds us nurses that our efforts to care for someone, regardless of the outcome, are not in vain.

Put Your Feet Up

After spraining my ankle at work, I was headed out west for a long-awaited vacation. The injury happened less than an hour before the end of my shift and caused me a lot of distress. I had been planning on hiking a lot during that vacation, and now I didn't know if I'd even be able to easily walk through the airport. It was an untimely accident, but nothing was going to prevent me from making that trip.

No professional courtesies were extended to me in the ER of the hospital where I worked when I hurt my ankle. I was told it would be a long time before I was examined, regardless of the fact that my injury happened while I was on duty. I headed to a clinic not far from where I lived; many hours were wasted before I eventually got to bed. It was confirmed that my ankle was sprained and not broken. That was better news than it could have been, and I armed myself with a leg splint, ace wrap, and high-lacing hiking boots before I headed out on my trip the next day.

I didn't give the hospital or the employee health department much thought while I was on vacation. I hiked the best I could with a tightly ace-wrapped ankle and kept my leg up on a chaise lounge at other times. Not pursuing any course of workman's compensation, I did what I pleased. I felt that attempting to seek any workman's compensation was going to be fruitless. Why? Because the first thing the supervisor on duty said to me after witnessing the accident was not, "Are you okay?" Instead, she said, "You're wearing open-back clogs." Yes, I was. Technically, such clogs were "illegal" for staff in the hospital at that time. Close-backed clogs or ones with an ankle strap were required, if you wore that type of footwear. My shoes had nothing to do with my foot becoming entangled with the large foot break at the end of the bed as the equipment was being pushed through the hallway. Personally, I felt that if I was wearing clogs with a strap, the strap may have become more entangled with the brake pedal, possibly making the injury worse. Whatever—I wasn't going to argue with anyone about it. At that point, what had happened couldn't be undone.

When I arrived home, my husband told me that someone from the employee health department had been trying to reach me during the week and wanted me to come in to be examined. I rarely provided anyone with my cell phone number; I only gave out my home landline information. What part of "she's on vacation" did they not understand, when he told them I was on the west coast? My flight had arrived late, so I called the department the next day. The person with whom I spoke was insisting that she wanted to examine me. Standing my ground, I emphasized that I was not going to drive forty-five minutes each way in order to have her look at my ankle for five minutes and then tell me, "It's fine, you're free to work tomorrow." I knew it would be a complete waste of my time and my last vacation day. I told her the ankle was still a little sore; I didn't feel the need to inform her that I had done some light hiking on it all week. It didn't appear to matter what I said to her; she was going to inform my manager to expect me at work the next night. But there was one other thing she suggested to me, which made me shake my head in disgust.

The staff member stated, "During your shift, try to put your feet up as much as possible."

I couldn't refrain from responding, "*Really?* You do know I work in an ICU, don't you?"

She reuttered something to the effect of me trying to keep my foot elevated whenever possible.

Okay, anyone who has ever been a nurse and is reading this, feel free to laugh loudly. We all know that nurses are usually on their feet *a lot*. Regardless of where a nurse is employed, the employee health staff's comment was a very unrealistic statement. When my husband was once a patient in an ER, he watched one of the RNs doing her job.

He commented to me, "She never sits down. She's

always moving, doing something." I reminded him that's how it was for me when I worked in the hospital. Nurses spend most of their eight- or twelve-hour shift on their feet.

Needless to say, I barely sat down that entire Friday night at work. The only time I sat with my foot elevated on another chair was during my dinner break. To make matters worse, I was assigned to two patients who were at completely opposite ends of the unit. Usually, patients who were in close proximity to each other were assigned together, if possible. Such was not the case that shift. I wish I had worn a pedometer to record exactly how many steps I took during the night, because it was a lot. My foot was extremely swollen when I left work, and it tremendously ached. *Sit and put your feet up. Yeah, right.* That wasn't possible last night, and it was going to happen when I returned to work Saturday night, either.

I rarely called out sick, maybe once a year, but that's what I did that night. I didn't care. My foot was injured because of something that happened on the job. I wasn't shown any mercy with the assignment that required me to walk back and forth through the entire length of the unit all night. Hospital management always did what was best for itself, so I did what was best for me. Sometimes things happen that way.

Merger

Rumors regarding a hospital merger were finally confirmed to us during a staff meeting. Two hospitals in the state were being combined to form one large new corporation. Services were going to be consolidated in order to reduce competing or duplication of services. That greatly affected CVT-S because it had been determined that our "sister" hospital was now going to become the solitary home of the cardiothoracic surgical program. Despite our phenomenal care and patient satisfaction survey results, the larger trauma center was going to take and absorb our future clientele.

Disheartened and beyond upset, we were scared to face what futures may be in store for us. We wanted things to remain the same, but no amount of wishing or praying was going to make that happen. Upper management had already made their decisions, and were not going to change their minds, especially because it affected the new corporation financially.

One of the biggest problems for us was that our sister hospital was a union-based facility, and we were not. Although we could apply for jobs in the new CVT-S type unit which they were building at the other hospital, we were given no guarantees. In fact, most of us were facing losing seniority and pay. We were being demoted and would be practically treated as new employees. This meant that we would earn very little vacation time and would have last choice on which days off we desired. We would be first to "float" to other areas within that hospital, and we would be last to be considered for picking up extra shifts in order to earn additional pay. Overall, we were presented with a poor, insulting offer after being dedicated nurses for many, many years.

Upon being told I would be placed in the category of nurses with only zero to five years of experience, I was completely disgusted. August marked my twentieth year of working in my current hospital environment. Yes, I once left for brief time, but I returned with my seniority intact and then remained a critical care nurse. The new situation was completely unfair, and I didn't know what I was going to do.

After much agonizing and a little bit of praying, I was presented with an option I hadn't ever considered. A friend called me at work one night and described a job and opportunity for which she thought I'd be well suited. It was a job in a new e-ICU in Massachusetts, and we'd be working under our former CVT-S manager. She had recently left to take a new managerial position and needed to hire RNs with critical care experience. This manager was unable to actively recruit nurses from where I was working, but somehow my friend found out about the job openings. We scheduled a group interview to learn more about what the job entailed.

An "e-ICU" is an electronic or "virtual" ICU. It falls under the realm of what people now call Telehealth medicine. Working in an off-site location in a corporate office building, we would have access to electronic patient charts. We would also be able to see real-time active telemetry rhythms and vital signs. Utilizing two-way cameras which were installed in the ICUs, we could speak face to face with the nurses or patients. The cameras, which also allowed us to perform patient assessments, had amazing visual acuity and magnification capabilities. We could read something as small as the date on a quarter which was placed on a patient's bed. This ability was demonstrated to us during our training. Some of our duties included chart auditing, but we were mostly considered the "second set of eyes" which helped to promote patient safety. We were also going to be a liaison between an ICU RN and a doctor who was scheduled to work with us each night. The MD was given the privileges of being able to write orders for any of the hospital ICUs covered under this new healthcare system. There would be a multitude of duties assigned to us each night, but it sounded like a unique and interesting job.

Mary's retirement party
Front row (left to right): Mary, Karen, Ann, MaryAnn
Back row (left to right): Julie, Bethany, Nancy, Allison

Better yet, the pay was phenomenal. Both the base pay as well as shift differentials were quite an increase over what I was currently earning. Incidentally, the job that was offered consisted of the same type and amount of twelve-hour night shifts and weekends which I presently worked and preferred. Without hesitating, I agreed to this new employment.

I was delving into a relatively new area of nursing that many people knew little about. I was scared but willing to try it. That was a major reason why I was glad that I had worked at the "baby hospital" for a brief time. It gave me the courage to once again pursue something which was a little out of the ordinary for me. I was not going to be coerced into staying in my current job that was evolving in a manner that didn't make me happy. In the past, I overcame my fears of employment change, and I could do it again. Armed with fortitude earned from choices and failures from the past, I took a leap of faith and became an e-ICU nurse.

You're a Nurse First

Even though we received a decent amount of training from someone who specialized in that field, I was nervous as the e-ICU "go live" day approached. I would be working the first shift when our unit started functioning mostly in the capacity it was intended. The doctors who were hired or required to work with us hadn't been fully credentialed to work in hospitals other than their own. I don't know what was completely involved with the paperwork, but apparently it was complicated. The decision was to "go live" so we could start to gain proficiency with the technology and become less hesitant while using it. A friend of mine used to say, "Just rip the Band-aid off." This meant to proceed without hesitancy and complete something that needs to be done, because postponing it and doing it slowly usually promoted anxiety. We all needed to work our first shift in the e-ICU at some point, and my initial experience would be over and done in a matter of hours. Not staying around to hold my hand and guide me every step of the way, the company representative who trained us told me before she walked out the door, "You'll be fine, everyone feels the way you do at first." She had to catch a plane in the morning and travel to another state because of training elsewhere. "You can always call me anytime if you have questions," she stated while departing.

The technology didn't always function perfectly. Sometimes this was due to the particular system, and sometimes it was because of user error. At times, certain steps needed to be performed in a specific manner. At all costs, we wanted to avoid having our face "frozen" on a screen in a patient's room. Sometimes we started talking without realizing that the "mute" button was still active. Worse than that was knowing that someone forgot to place the microphone on mute, and something was said that shouldn't have been heard. Mistakes were sometimes made; it was inevitable. But we were always reminded, "You're a nurse, first. Don't worry about the technology." We were hired for our nursing experience and expertise, not our computer skills. Many of the nurses who were hired for the job didn't grow up with a cell phone in our hands or take computer classes in high school. We may have had some basic computer knowledge, but that's not what the e-ICU needed from us. They employed nurses who could recognize patient problems and were competent in adult critical care issues.

I survived my first night without incident. Maybe

I should have enjoyed those nights more than I did. We were working without a doctor present for several months, and the hospital nurses didn't have much need to call us. Being a nurse, we couldn't write orders; we could only make recommendations. Often, our suggestions were rejected or we were completely ignored. Many of the nurses in the hospitals did not embrace the concept of an e-ICU. They thought we were somehow stealing their jobs, and negative propaganda was spread about us. The clinical nurses didn't know we were also experienced RNs, and many of them didn't respect us. I empathized with how they probably felt, but sometimes the rude behavior was difficult to tolerate. Despite how we were treated or what was said to us, we needed to act as professionals and remember that the various hospitals were our "customers." Sometimes nurses said terrible things about us as we were in the process of "exiting" out of a room. As the camera was being shut off and turning away from the nurse, audio was still available, and we heard what was said. Even if it was mentioned casually, it was tiresome when people kept referring to us with comments like, "Big Brother is watching." As a joke, I suggested that the song "Every Breath You Take" by the band The Police be adopted as our e-ICU theme song.

If I still worked in Providence and an e-ICU system was installed in our ICUs, I can certainly imagine how I and my colleagues would have felt. It would have probably been insulting to have someone appear on a screen in the patient's room, questioning what was happening or asking if we needed assistance. We would have assumed they thought we weren't capable of taking care of our patients. With many years of experience, we didn't need help from a stranger who we didn't know or trust. Besides, we had plenty of doctor coverage twenty-four hours a day; there was no shortage of assistance for us.

But many hospitals are not affiliated with medical schools or utilize Interns and Residents. The smaller, private hospitals with their own group of attending physicians did need help at night. No one doctor can work all day and every day, and it wasn't fair to those doctors to be called at home in the middle of the night to be asked for simple orders. Once doctors were finally allowed to join our team, the e-ICU provided a good service, enabling nurses to obtain certain orders on a timely basis. We tried to use the cameras judiciously, not in an obnoxious way. Real time assessments by an MD became an invaluable tool.

Through access to electronic charting, lab values, and radiology images and reports, we were able to avert many problems the patients may encounter. We treated abnormal hematology and electrolyte values. IV fluid or medication could be ordered if a patient was hypotensive. If a patient was having a CVA, stroke protocols were initiated faster. Our physicians were leaders in code blue situations, and we ordered EKGs and notified the cardiologists if someone was having chest pain. While the hospital's nurses were performing their duties in a code or an emergency situation, the e-ICU could make camera rounds on the remaining ICU patients. Trying to prevent harm to anyone, the e-ICU nurses could call and say, "We know you're really busy in that room, but your IV pump infusing the vasopressor in another room is beeping; you've run out of medication." Or we might catch a patient trying to crawl out of bed, so we'd say, "That patient in bed number nine is being naughty and might fall; you need to send someone to check on him." It rarely happened, but we did witness a patient coding in one room while a different patient started coding in another room within the same ICU.

I could go on and on about how the e-ICU helped other ICUs under our watch. And no, none of those nurses ever lost their jobs because of us. As the "second set of eyes," we could not do the physical part of the job, and therefore could never replace any of them. There were certain nights some of us wished we could jump through the TV or computer screen and physically help them. It was difficult sitting back and watching them struggle with a code or an IV insertion or short staffing when we knew we had skills or an unused set of hands to hold or help a patient. We became frustrated witnessing how patients sometimes treated their nurses despite how hard they were working. It also saddened us when patients died. Our empathy and level of humanity wasn't diminished because we sat at a desk with screens and a keyboard. In fact, most of us greatly appreciated our e-ICU jobs and became even more aware of how tirelessly RNs in hospitals work through what we saw via our cameras.

Eventually, some of the nurses in the hospitals began to trust us more and utilized the doctor on duty quite a bit. We enjoyed "working" with many of them, and we each had our favorites. Some hospital nurses were determined to not be friendly toward us, but that was their problem. Many of us, after years of working in the e-ICU, couldn't understand how they held onto animosity for so long. It must be exhausting and use so much negative energy being hostile. Isn't it easier to smile and be pleasant?

This was the start of my new venture into a unique niche of critical care nursing. The 45th e-ICU in the United States was opened in Massachusetts, and I was part of its beginning, slightly prior to its initial shifts.

Dr. Sam

I considered myself fortunate to be working with an extremely intelligent group of MDs in the e-ICU. Most of them were not only Intensivists, but also had a sub-specialty such as pulmonology, infectious disease, or anesthesia medicine. Collectively, they had many years of medical experience and several of them worked in some very well-known, Boston-area hospitals. A few of the doctors were also educators, and I learned a lot from them. They seemed to love sharing their wealth of knowledge if asked to explain something related to medicine. Other doctors widely read research material and were always up to date on the latest diseases and medical practices. It was amazing how much I continued to learn by being employed in that job.

As with any job, I preferred to work more with certain doctors, and less with others. My schedule was made well in advance, and then I would find out later which doctor I would be working with on a given night. Therefore, I looked forward to some nights, but not others. There weren't many doctors whom I disliked, only an occasional one or two. I'm sure they felt the same way about the nurses, including me.

There was one physician named Dr. Sam who was well liked by everyone in the e-ICU and the hospitals we served. But that was somewhat a problem at times. This MD was extremely handsome, and all the nurses agreed on that fact. The RNs in one of the hospital ICUs were particularly fond of him. When they knew he was working, they'd activate what was called the "e-Alert" button which signaled they wanted us to camera in to a particular ICU room. It became fairly apparent that they were frequently hitting this red button because they wanted to speak to and look at this doctor. There was rarely a true emergency; they simply wanted a little "eye candy" to break up the monotony of their night. I never saw bigger grins from those nurses than when he was on camera in their rooms.

Maybe he realized what they were doing, maybe not. Part of the appeal of this doctor was that he was not only handsome. He was humble, never became angry or impatient with any of us, and spoke softly and eloquently. He was very intelligent, yet he was not snobbish about his intellect or physical features. If possible, we would have nominated him for sainthood. None of us were surprised when one day he showed us a photo of his fiancé. She was extremely beautiful and could have been the winner of the Miss Universe pageant. I'm sure she was equally talented, as well.

In the meantime, we almost always took an abundance of live video requests from that one particular hospital when he was on duty with us. Who's the lucky nurse tonight who is paired up with that ICU? Dr. Sam is working tonight.

Unfortunately for us, he left the healthcare system where we worked and moved out of state. Many doctors came and left our healthcare division in Massachusetts over the years. He was one of the "good ones" with whom we definitely missed working. I wonder if any of the male doctors with whom I worked will read this brief tale and ponder about who I am writing. I don't gamble, but I bet the female nurses who were employed with me know the answer to this mystery.

DEN Gate 99

I can't explain it, but sometimes it seems that when I'm in public, elderly people gravitate toward me. Do they have poor eyesight and mistake me for someone related to them? Maybe I look familiar to them in some other way. Perhaps they feel safe standing next to a tall woman. I'll never know the answers to these questions, but I have a theory which came to me while I was traveling on vacation.

Heading home from my trip, I had a lengthy layover in Denver airport. This is one airport in which I don't mind having extra time between flights. I find I'm usually dropped off at a gate numbered in the single digits, and then I have to hurry to catch my connecting flight at the complete opposite end of the terminal. Often, I've had to run to make my next flight on time. But today, I leisurely strolled to my connecting gate area, which was number 99. I didn't mind the long walk because it gave me an opportunity to stretch my legs before sitting in a cramped airline seat for four hours. When I reached gate 99, the area was fairly vacant, and I had my choice of almost anywhere I wanted to sit. I chose a seat with a good view through a huge window, and which had a solid wall behind it. Making myself as comfortable as possible, I took out my paperback book and started to read.

Occasionally looking up from my book, I saw there wasn't a lot of activity near me. It was nice to be able to read without many distractions. I enjoyed people-watching, but it was too quiet for that activity until the next plane was ready to be boarded.

Eventually, one lone figure was heading in my direction. It was an elderly woman, moving methodically and slowly. Trying not to be obvious, I watched her as she moved closer and closer in my direction. Upon arriving at gate 99, she looked around, deciding where to sit. I silently giggled to myself. *Lady, I'm the only person sitting here. You can have absolutely any other seat you want; they're all available.* Much to my surprise, she continued walking toward me, and sat down right next to me. *Seriously?* I enjoy having a little elbow room and personal space. But somehow, I thought it was rude to abruptly get up and move to another chair as she sat down.

Appearing friendly, she smiled at me and said, "Good morning."

After smiling back and exchanging the greeting with her, I continued reading my book. Out of the corner of my eye, I could see her rummaging through her pocket-book. She found her glasses, and accidentally dropped them on the floor. After picking them up, she pulled a book out of her bag. The paperback also dropped on the floor, after first bouncing off my foot. I picked it up and handed it to her as she apologized to me. Next, she located her snack, a fresh red apple. Alas, the woman who couldn't seem to hold onto anything she touched also dropped the piece of fruit. I watched as the apple silently rolled over the airport carpeting and under the row of seats in front of us. She stood up and retrieved the fruit, and I was somewhat expecting her to throw it in the nearby trash can. But, by guessing her age, I figured it was more likely that she wouldn't want to waste food, which was something I could completely understand. I figured she'd throw the apple back in her bag or go wash it off in the bathroom. She did neither. After rubbing it a little on her pant leg after she sat down, she proceeded to take a large bite and eat the whole thing except for the core.

Yuck. I was more than grossed out thinking about the amount of foot traffic and rolling suitcases which that airport carpet has seen. The carpeting may have looked vacuumed and clean, but there were a million unseen germs lurking on it. I watched her eating and thoroughly enjoying her snack. She was totally unaware of what I was thinking. Then, I had to smile to myself. I'm sure she wasn't, but the woman looked like she could have been well over 100 years old. No wonder she has lived so long; she was probably immune to every germ on the planet. Certainly, an apple rolling across a dirty carpet wasn't going to kill her.

Why did she sit next to me when she could have comfortably sat anywhere else? I'll share my theory. Unbeknownst to me, I think someone must have tattooed "geriatric nurse" on my forehead with invisible ink. Of course, the ink is only invisible to me, but is as bright as a neon sign to anyone over the age of eighty. I must have been sporting that tattoo for a number of years, which is why elderly people gravitate toward me. Oh well. Maybe kindness toward older people is a gift I can share with the world.

Ring the Doorbell

I've known and worked with a lot of funny people over the years, and I love it when someone has a great sense of humor. I'm not talking about people who have a contrived sort of humor or who feel they have to say something witty in every situation. Being around people like that bores me and listening to it becomes tedious after a short while. Rather, I enjoy spontaneous comments which tickle my funny bone, especially when humor is not totally intentional. I specifically remember a couple of funny nurses, the dynamic duo of Brian and Kevin. Individually, they usually made me laugh, but watch out when they were both on shift together.

On a warm summer evening, I went to work and saw the hospital where Brian and Kevin worked listed under my name. They were both on duty that night, as well, which was a good thing. Both being competent nurses, they took excellent care of their patients and made appropriate phone calls to the e-ICU when necessary. Occasionally, Brian would call on the phone to chat with me for a couple minutes, especially if he was having a terrible night. He was one of the few nurses on "the other side of the camera" who remembered that I was also once a critical care nurse who worked in a hospital. I understood how he might feel about things such as challenging patients, management issues, or a colleague who could be driving you crazy at times. It was always good talking with him, and I hoped our brief conversations gave him a little encouragement or positivity if he ever needed it.

During this weekend night, Brian gave me a quick phone call to vent some frustrations. He told me that the air conditioning wasn't working in the ICU, and it was hotter than "you know what." The patients were sweating, and the nurses were sweating. Portable fans were set up in the patients' rooms, but they weren't very effective. It was muggy and everyone felt gross and miserable. The environmental working conditions that night sounded horrendous. I never enjoyed it when a patient needed a fan in his or her room; my hair would get blown in my face. If a patient coughed or sneezed, that was probably blown at me, as well. But the comfort of the patient exceeded the desires of the nurse, so I tolerated it and sometimes wore a facemask.

Brian continued by saying, "So that's why I wanted to call you. Make sure you ring the doorbell when you camera into a room. Because it's so hot in here, we're all working naked and you might see something you don't want to see. Give us a little warning first, okay?"

Totally not expecting him to say anything like that, I instantly started laughing. "No problem, thanks for letting me know," I said as I hung up the phone.

Since I continued to laugh, my fellow e-ICU nurses were curious as to what he said. Only Brian would say something like that to me, and he knew I wasn't going to be offended. He probably needed a good laugh, too, and enjoyed my lighthearted reaction. Thankfully, I didn't have to camera in to any of his rooms that night.

Adopt-a-Family

Most nurses realize they are paid well. As times change, we all desire cost-of-living raises, or annual merit-based pay increases. Sometimes nurses are not paid what they are worth, but we all certainly earn well above minimum wage. Shift and weekend differentials exist, and extra pay is given to "charge nurses." Usually there is plenty of overtime or extra shifts available for us to add to our income. It was mind-blowing to consider that as I was standing at work, I was earning a dollar a minute or more. How many people in this country work two or three jobs and still don't make as much money as a nurse may earn in a year?

Christmas was the time of year when I knew many of my colleagues thought about these things. Instead of solely spending money on ourselves, families, or close friends, we usually also "adopted" a family. Either

My last New Year's Eve shift at work in the e-ICU,
January 1, 2021

through a local church organization, school, or word of mouth, we found a family or two who had financial needs. We'd learn the ages, clothing sizes, and desires of the family we adopted, then proceeded to buy them things according to a wishlist.

A couple nurses in the e-ICU, Kathy and Mary-Ann, organized the Christmas donations the last year we worked together. They had contacted an inner-city school in Providence and collaborated with one of the staff members. The nurses received a list of the desired items we were asked to purchase. As Kathy described to us what was requested, most of us were amazed and touched by the simplicity of the things that were both wanted and needed. We were asked to purchase non-perishable food and healthcare items such as soap, toothpaste, and toothbrushes. After our goods were collected, the staff at the school would determine who were the neediest families and would divide up our purchases among them. Could any of us in the e-ICU refuse such simple requests? Our adopted families were not seeking expensive video games or electronic toys. They weren't asking for bicycles or brand-name clothing. Only items which took care of a person's basic needs were being asked of us.

We had a couple of weeks in order to obtain items we each wished to give to the families. As Christmas approached, we watched boxes and bags pile up in our e-ICU conference room as things were donated. I think the whole nursing staff contributed, as well as many of the doctors with whom we worked. We had collected an array of bath and beauty products as well as food. Several nurses, understanding that children need to have fun at Christmas, gave things which were not on the request list. I noticed a few bags of candy wrapped in brightly colored foil, other sweet treats, and a few small toys and clothing accessories.

It made me proud knowing that I worked with such a generous group of people. We all knew how to spend money on ourselves, but we showed we could be generous to strangers, as well. Both MaryAnn and Kathy's vehicles were probably completely full as they packed up the gifts and brought them to the school in Providence shortly before Christmas. Kathy told us that the staff member at the school was amazed at the quantity of gifts and that she didn't expect such a big response to her request for items. At a later date, we did receive a handwritten thank you note from someone at that school.

That was our last kind deed as a group of nurses in the e-ICU. Little did we know that in the near future we were all going to be forced to go our separate ways and once again redefine our careers.

Conference Call

One of the benefits of working in the e-ICU was being able to call in to work and participate in a staff meeting. Whether we had Bluetooth capabilities in our car or called from home, we could enter a code number and be connected to the conference room where the meeting took place. Most of us called and simply placed the phone on mute while we listened to what was being discussed. At least we had the opportunity to listen, ask questions, or contribute our thoughts on work matters. I rarely physically joined the staff meeting, since it was an hour drive from where I lived. If my shift was ending and the staff meeting was starting, I called from my car in the parking lot and listened while driving home. I'd be at least half the distance home before the meeting ended, and sleep time was precious to me—especially if I had to return to work that same night. Participating in the staff meeting was something I almost always did, especially because we were paid for the time we called in on the phone.

An upcoming staff meeting invitation was sent to us via email. I had thought about listening to it via phone, but I made other plans, instead. The weather was supposed to be conducive to a safe hike in the White Mountains of New Hampshire, and I wanted to go snowshoeing. I had completed hiking all of the required forty-eight mountain peaks which are over 4000 feet tall to become a member of the AMC's 4000-Footer Club. At that point, I was working on what is known as the "Winter Forty-eight." I wanted to tackle Mt. Cabot, the northernmost White Mountain on the list. While getting a very early start in order to reach the trailhead and complete the five-hour drive before sunrise, I contemplated whether I would call in to the meeting or not.

Only a few miles from the access road to the trail-head of Mt. Cabot, I received a phone call while I was waiting at a stoplight. It was one of the day shift nurses, Kathy, who was calling me. Glad she was able to reach me, she reminded me about the staff meeting and told me it was now considered "mandatory attendance." She said she thought we were all going to be told we were losing our jobs. The previous day, she explained, someone from upper management had arrived in the e-ICU, and a private meeting with our manager and a few others was held in the conference room with the doors closed. After the conclusion of the meeting, the people in attendance left without saying anything else to the nurses who were on duty at the time. The mysterious meeting had led staff to believe we were going to receive bad news.

I thanked Kathy for calling me and said I would find a safe place to pull over on the road. I would call in to the meeting in a couple of minutes.

By the time I found a safe area in which to stop and dial all the access numbers, the meeting had already begun. I continued driving once I was connected, thinking that I might lose phone reception at any time in the remote area where I was located. After making it to the parking area at the base of the mountain, I shut off the car engine and listened.

Indeed, we were all losing our jobs as of April 1st. Was that irony missed by anyone? April Fool's, the joke's on all of you who thought you still had some job security for a few more years. It was difficult to believe we were actually hearing the words which said we only had a few months left of employment in the e-ICU. Our jobs were all being relocated to a huge new corporate building situated in Texas. We were told a job was still available to anyone who wanted to relocate to that state. Other than that, not much was promised to assist us in our new predicament. Most of the staff were upset but remained silent. When the meeting ended, I sat motionless in my car for a few minutes as tears silently rolled down my cheeks. Incredibly timed, the song "Easy Come, Easy Go" by the band Winger started playing on the car radio.

How appropriate for that moment in time. When the song was over, I called my husband and told him the news. He sounded even more shocked than I felt. Knowing I was upset, he asked if I was coming home. After getting up at one o'clock in the morning and driving so many hours, I told him I was still going hiking. The fresh cold air was what I needed to clear my mind, and solo hiking always provided me with the quiet time I needed to think about things. I didn't want to waste this precious day and opportunity to summit another mountain in winter. I said I'd see him later that night after the hike and drive back home was over.

Since we knew a new corporate center was built in Texas, most of the staff already knew we'd eventually all lose our jobs. It was only a matter of whether it happened sooner or later. Telehealth nursing's base of operation can be located anywhere. The healthcare system found a cheaper alternative than to continue paying the nurses who lived in a fairly expensive region of the country. In an impersonal way, we were notified we were dispensable, despite our hard work and dedication to make the e-ICU program thrive over the years. Considering the staff greatly ranged in age, different thoughts went through our minds as we heard the job loss news. A couple of the staff were close to retirement age, so they retired. Some nurses found ICU jobs in local hospitals. Others worked as nurses in different capacities which they hadn't considered in the past.

Ann on Mt. Cabot Summit

As for me, I briefly tried working in a full-time day shift job at a surgery center. I was immensely unhappy in that job for a multitude of reasons; I also had great difficulty making the transition from working a part-time night shift to a full-time day schedule. I quit after three months. The nursing staff who worked there were terrific to me, and it was the one reason I tried to perform that job as long as I could. But honestly, I was miserable every single day I worked there, and life is too short to live that way.

Happily, since then, I have reinvented myself and am fulfilling a dream of mine, which is to write books. I always wanted to be a published author before I died, and I now have that opportunity. Being unemployed has given me the time I always needed to place my thoughts and memories into print.

Mentors/Finale

While working as a nurse, you learn a lot about people and human nature. You also learn that life isn't fair. People may become ill with cancer, or a genetic or autoimmune disease. Sometimes a person's bad habits finally catch up with them, such as after taking street drugs or a lifetime of smoking. The most important things I learned as a nurse, however, were the things I learned about myself.

Thinking about the over-thirty years I spent as a nurse while writing this book was an eye-opening experience. There are countless nurses I've worked with, and I still remember many of their names. RNs who I hadn't thought about in years came back to mind. Some of those memories made me laugh, and others I'd rather forget. The majority of nurses I've worked with over the years have taught me many things, both good and bad. I knew who I wanted to emulate, and I also knew who I considered to be L-A-Z-Y—I hope I never have anyone like that taking care of me or any of my relatives. I don't think I ever properly thanked the nurses who were my mentors, but who never realized they were playing that role in my life.

I worked with a woman in Worcester who was a very independent person. She wasn't waiting around for a man to rescue her and provide her with a good life; she was doing that all on her own. She traveled solo around the country, often taking her bicycle with her so she could explore different areas and stay physically fit at the same time. Not living in fear of anything, she wasn't wasting one moment of life.

Another nurse I worked with in Worcester had a parttime job in the cardiothoracic ICU. I only worked there briefly as a SNI, but the time I spent in that unit solidified my desire to someday become an ICU nurse. This male nurse quizzed me on various things, such as, "How do you tell if someone is developing a tension pneumothorax?" I think he asked me the same things every week we worked together to see if I was paying attention. He didn't need to take the time to teach me anything, but I'm glad that he did.

There were other nurses with whom I worked who were incredibly smart. Several ICU nurses in Providence had earned their adult CCRN certificate. As a relatively new nurse, that was almost unfathomable. One of my future managers encouraged me to study for the test and take it. It was an annual goal for a couple years during my performance reviews. I'm glad she

The trail to Bondcliff, and Ann's outdoor office,
where creative ideas are born

kept encouraging me to take that test. It wasn't until I started studying for it that I realized how little I knew about certain medical topics. After successfully passing the test on my first attempt, I continued studying and also earned my cardiac surgical specialty certification. I was proud to already have those certificates when I applied for my e-ICU job.

Other nurses may have lacked advanced credentials, but they made up for it with their incredible compassion for all their patients. They demonstrated endless patience and provided care as if they were taking care of their own family member. Somehow, they managed to organize their time so they could speak with their patients and families in an unrushed manner that was comforting to everyone they met.

Some of my favorite nurses were the ones who were tough, but effective while providing care. They knew how to motivate patients and get them to participate in their own care in order to get better, faster. As I developed my own style of nursing, I hoped I was effective at doing the same thing. I didn't have to do it too often, but sometimes I said to a patient, "I'm your nurse; they're not paying me to be your friend. I hope you like me as a nurse, but my primary goal is to make sure you get well enough to leave this place." Somehow, I think saying that earned me a little more respect from the patient's perspective. Perhaps they believed I was sincere when I said those things.

That's just a sampling of the types of fantastic nurses I had the pleasure of knowing over the years. I could go on and on, mentioning the "Energizer bunny" nurses with endless stamina as well as the helpful staff who didn't let me flounder and drown when my assignment was overwhelming. I've been blessed by working with nurses who acted as a team under a multitude of different circumstances.

I hope everyone who reads this book will have many positive nursing experiences and get to know many incredible people as well. This statement applies whether you're starting your career as a nurse or if you're not in the medical field but become a patient someday. If you're at the end of your career, I hope you can look back and reflect on it without regrets. And possibly, if you've ever worked with me, you may recognize yourself in this book and smile.

My best wishes to all the nurses with whom I've ever worked, as well as all the other nurses in this world I've never met. Thank you for joining the nursing profession and making a difference in someone's life.

Abbreviations/ Glossary

ABG — Arterial Blood Gas. Measures oxygen, carbon dioxide, and acidity of blood. Drawn from an artery, not a vein.

A-Line — Arterial Line. Used to monitor blood pressure and draw blood for lab work and ABGs.

ACLS — Advanced Cardiac Life Support. More advanced care than is provided during BLS or CPR, it includes administration of life-saving medication.

AIDS/HIV — Acquired Immune Deficiency Syndrome, caused by the Human Immunodeficiency Virus.

Angiography — Liquid contrast is injected into the bloodstream to make blood vessels visible on a scan. An invasive procedure done to examine the blood vessels of the heart or other organs.

Arterial Waveform — The waveform produced on a cardiac monitor after being connected to an A-line.

Bony Prominences — Areas of the body at greatest risk for developing decubiti.

BLS — Basic Life Support.

Cardiologist — Doctor who specializes in conditions involving the heart.

Cardiothoracic Surgeon — Surgeon who specialized and operates on the heart or its major blood vessels and treats organs within the thoracic chest cavity.

Central Line — An invasive line placed under sterile procedures. It can be utilized for providing various vital signs, for infusing fluids or medications—including those which are irritating to blood vessels—or to obtain blood samples.

CVT-I — Cardiovascular Thoracic Step-Down Unit. An intermediate patient care area.

CVT-S — Cardiovascular Thoracic Surgical ICU.

CABG — Coronary Artery Bypass Graft. A cardiac surgical procedure.

Chest Tube — Drainage tube placed into the thoracic cavity for the purpose of removing air or fluid, or both.

Colostomy — An orifice created after a section of bowel is surgically removed; it is an opening in the abdomen. It is how waste products are eliminated from the body.

Decubiti — Skin breakdown, which is measured in different degrees, depending how deeply it affects the skin

e-ICU — Electronic Intensive Care Unit. A remotely operated critical care area which routinely uses two-way cameras to communicate with a nurse in a hospital ICU room. Considered Telehealth medicine.

ECG — Electrocardiogram. A way to monitor the waveform pattern and speed of the heart.

EKG — Electrocardiogram A term sometimes used interchangeably with ECG but actually refers to a 12-Lead EKG obtained from a portable machine. This shows various waveforms produced by the heart.

Foley Catheter — A brand-name urinary catheter inserted into a person to drain urine.

FSC — Fitchburg State College in Massachusetts. Currently known as Fitchburg State University.

Isolation Room — A patient room requiring someone to wear personal protective gear, which varies depending on the infection or disease.

JCAHO — Joint Commission on Accreditation of Healthcare Organizations. An organization that conducts inspections of hospitals. Their accreditation may be required for a hospital to receive Medicaid and Medicare reimbursements.

Mandible — The lower jawbone in the face.

Night Shift — An eight- or twelve-hour overnight shift, typically from 11 p.m. to 7:30 a.m. or 7 p.m. to 7:30 a.m. Hours may vary slightly according to individual hospitals.

Passy Muir Valve — A special cap which is placed over

a tracheostomy and allows a person's speech to be audibly heard. It is removable, and cannot be used simultaneously while a patient is on a ventilator.

Pin Care — Care provided to external pins used for bone traction devices to prevent infection.

Pleur-evac — Brand-name device which provides suction and is connected to a chest tube.

Preceptor — A nurse who orients a new employee to the ICU. Orientation may be several weeks or months. They guide, demonstrate, and teach the new employee the ways of the ICU. A checklist is often utilized to ensure the new employee has demonstrated competency in various skills.

Telehealth — Healthcare which is provided remotely via a communication device such as a camera.

Tracheostomy — An alternate airway which facilitates unobstructed breathing. Located in the neck. It may be connected to a ventilator by utilizing a tracheostomy tube.

Ventilator — A breathing machine connected to a tracheostomy or endotracheal tube in an intubated patient. Different modes of ventilation are used depending on the illness or respiratory needs of the patient. This is considered to be a life-sustaining device.

Acknowledgements

Thank you to Steven Porter at Stillwater River Press for his valuable guidance to me as a new writer. He propelled my transition from being a nurse to a published author with sensitivity, skill, and speed. My publication goal was achieved through his meticulous and timely editing. Christina Bagni was also a part of the talented editing team. Elisha Gillette created the unique exterior cover design, which conveyed the essence of how I wanted my book to be depicted. Dawn Porter coordinated multiple tasks throughout the entire publication process.

I cherish the enthusiasm and encouragement I received from my former colleagues after they learned I had written a book about my nursing career. Too many to name individually, both night and day shift staff associated with my employment in Providence and Westwood have my love and gratitude.

Special thanks to Bob Finn who patiently listened to me whenever I mentioned my book endeavor. His humor, uplifting responses, and astute marketing suggestions were always appreciated.

Finally, thank you to author Louella Eastwood, whom I met at the Rhode Island Author/Writer Expo in 2022. She told me, "Last year, I was standing where you are." Then, pointing me in the direction of Steven Porter, she urged me to follow my dreams of publishing a book.

About the Author

Raised in South Deerfield, Massachusetts, Ann pursued a career as a nurse and graduated from Fitchburg State College with a Bachelor of Science degree in Nursing. She primarily worked in various ICUs for 30 years. Showing dedication to her area of expertise, she earned both her adult Critical Care RN and Cardiac Surgery specialty certificates.

Seeking challenges outside of the workplace, Ann obtained her private and commercial pilot licenses, in both single and multiengine airplanes.

Presently keeping her feet on the ground, she travels, hikes, and climbs mountains whenever possible. Conquering all 48 summits in the White Mountains of NH which are above 4000 feet in elevation, she is a member of the AMC's 4000-Footer club. Photography, birding, and cooking are her other favorite hobbies.

Ann currently lives in Rhode Island with her husband, Wayne, and her rescue dog.

Made in the USA
Middletown, DE
11 August 2023